AF822211

Mike Nielsen

Precision Timing for All Instruments

advance music | The Jazz Handbook Series

Mike Nielsen

Precision Timing for All Instruments

The Ultimate Rhythm Workout

advance music

This book is dedicated to my parents Carl and Sonja who have given me endless support throughout the years.

Cover design: Elke Dörr
Recording credits: Mike Nielsen – Guitar
Recorded and engineered by Mike Nielsen

Printed in Germany

ADV 13284
ISMN 979-0-2063-0991-5
ISBN 978-3-95481-018-5

Table of Contents

The audio recording is an integral part of this book which originally included a CD.

Audio files can be downloaded for free with the following voucher code on **www.schott-music.com/online-material**: **5Ti3oNmN**

Preface

This book is a result of my study of odd metre, metric modulation and subdivision. Accurate timing is synonymous with great music and with great players. Odd metre is a vast subject and forms the basis of many music cultures, for example Bulgarian music. Odd metre is essentially an odd number of beats per bar. Seven eighth notes may be subdivided into an eighth note grouping of 2-2-3, which can be seen as a time signature of 7/8 or 3½/4. In Bulgarian music the *Lesnoto* – a seven-beat cycle – is subdivided into 3-2-2, and the *Kopanitsa* – an eleven-beat cycle – into 2-2-3-2-2.

Musicians today are required to perform odd metre songs; it is a subject that must be studied and internalised with no easy solutions. With practice it will become as natural as playing in 4/4 or 3/4 time. Spending time with a metronome, drum machine or better still a group, is essential to acquiring odd metre fluency. This book will give the tools for odd metre development.

Metric modulation occurs when performing in a whole number ratio with an existing time signature, for example, the common 3:2 modulation, where three beats are played in the space of two (2/4), or in the compound time signature of 6/8, where two metres of two and six occur simultaneously. Metric modulation knowledge is essential for creative playing and composition – it promotes good time and flowing expressive lines. The tempo of a metric modulation is also in a whole number ratio with the original tempo of a time signature. If a tempo in 2/4 is 40 beats per minute (bpm), and three beats are played in the same time frame, then both tempi are moving at a 3:2 relationship or 60:40 bmp. Therefore, metric modulation is in fact two metres moving simultaneously at different speeds. The ability to recognise various metric modulations is one of the goals of working with this book. Higher ratio numbers give more complex mathematical divisions, and therefore the more complex the relationship between the metric modulation and the original tempo becomes.

Odd metre, metric modulation and subdivision practice are the keys to precision timing and will give the player a lot more freedom and accuracy within the common tempi of 4/4 and 3/4.

The best of luck

Mike Nielsen

Acknowledgements

Thanks to Marta for putting up with my early morning disappearing act during the writing of this book. And to Oskar and Harriet who are just wonderful. I would like to thank Bret Willmott, Professor at Berklee College of Music, Boston, who introduced me to the subject of odd metre and metric modulation way back in the early 80's, and my colleagues Ronan and Conor Guilfoyle, with whom I spent many hours practising in a small drum room in Newpark Music Centre; where oxygen became scarce but where enthusiasm never waned. I am very grateful to Dr. Ita Beausang who edited many drafts of this book with a smile and a prayer.

Chapter 1

Division of the Beat: Accurate Eighth Note Timing

Set a metronome at 80 bpm and start with tapping your foot evenly on the down beat and speak the Indian syllables *Ta-Ka* written above the notes and discussed in chapter 2. The object of the exercises below is to internalise even eighth note beats. The value of the following exercise should not be taken lightly – it is the key to proper timing and promotes a solid internal rhythmic sense. Remember both the down beat *Ta* and the up beat, *Ka* are of equal importance.

Practise the exercises at slow and fast tempi.

Ex. 1

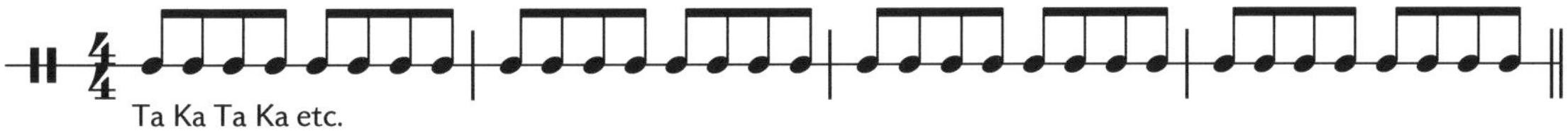

When the above exercise is performed evenly practise it leaving out the *Ta* (saying it silently) as shown in Ex. 2 below, and concentrate on the *Ka*.

Ex. 2

The next exercise and following exercises are recognised *Latin rhythms*. Ex. 3 is a repeated figure used in Cuban music called the *clave* (Klah-veh). This is a *3-2 son clave* – three rhythmic accents in the first bar and two in the second bar. Clap the rhythm and speak the Indian syllables *Ta* for quarter notes and *Ta-Ka* for eighth notes. To accurately count a rhythm it is important to count the rests. Build up to a tempo of 200 bpm.

Ex. 3

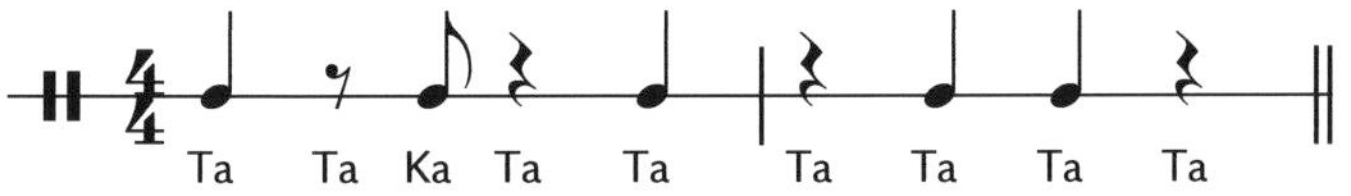

The next step is to set your metronome at 100 bpm and tap your foot on beats one and three. The rhythm will move at the same speed over the beat value of two beats (2/2). The beat unit is a half note which contains four eighth notes; therefore Indian syllables for a group of four are used: *Ta-Ka-Di-Mi*, (twice as fast as the quarter notes) and *Ta-Ka* for quarter notes. See Ex. 4 below:

Ex. 4

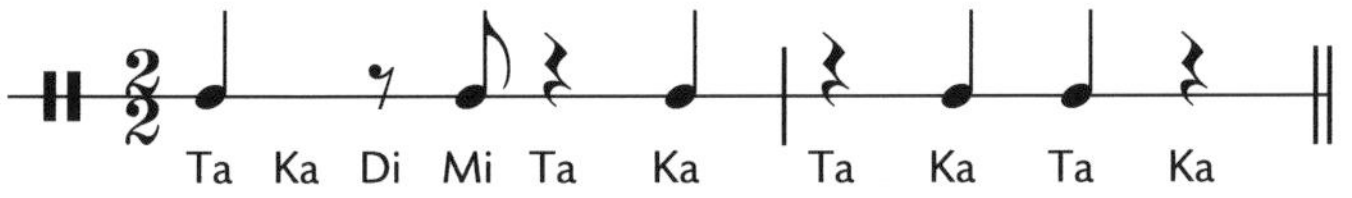

When you are comfortable with exercises 3 and 4 above, reverse the bars as shown below which illustrate a 2-3 *clave.*

Ex. 5

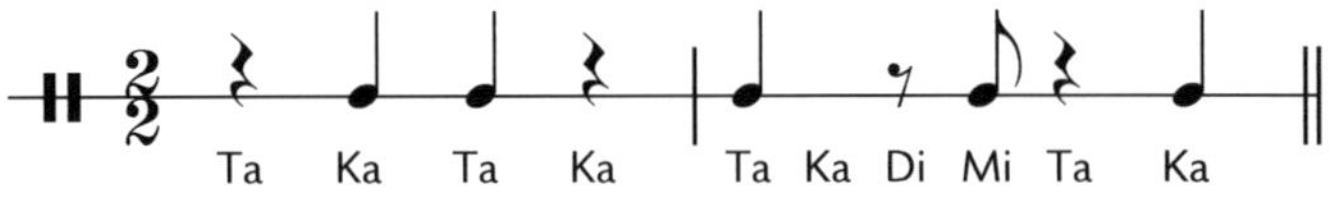

The following example in 4/4 time is a 3-2 *Rumba clave*. Practise the reverse – 2-3 also. Then apply the same principle of reversing the bars to the next series of exercises.

Ex. 6

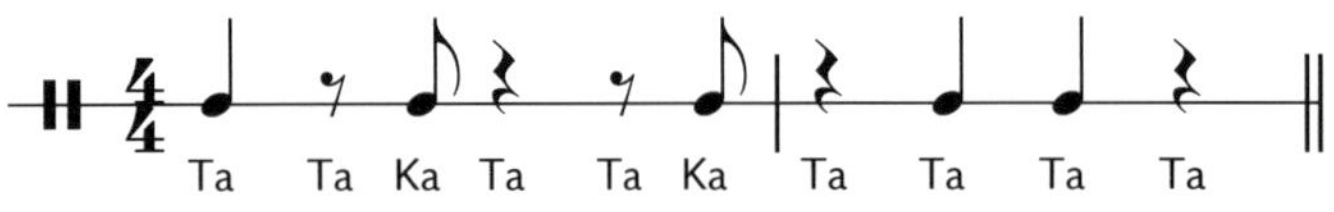

The following example is a *Brazilian clave*:

Ex. 7

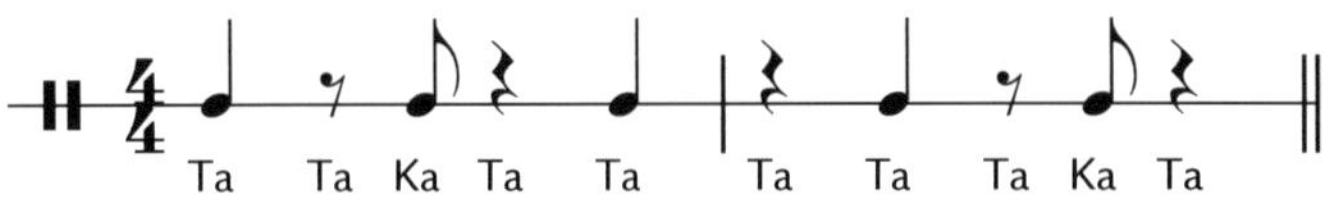

The following example is a *Cáscara* pattern:

Ex. 8

The following example shows typical accented beats in the *Cáscara* pattern:

Ex. 9

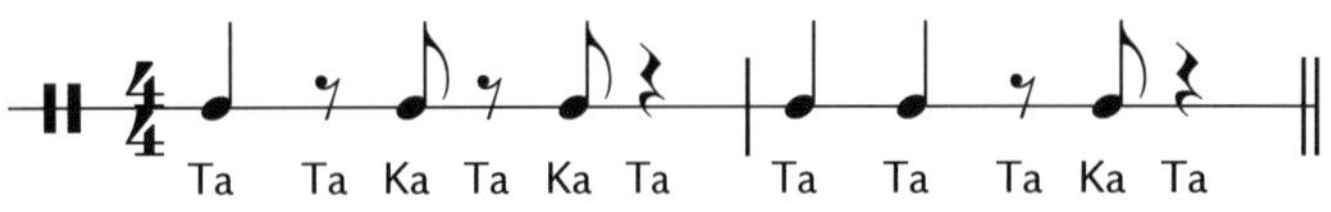

Ex. 10 below shows the *3-2 son clave* and the *Cáscara* pattern together. Record the *clave* while you clap the *Cáscara* pattern. Then tap both rhythms simultaneously.

Ex. 10

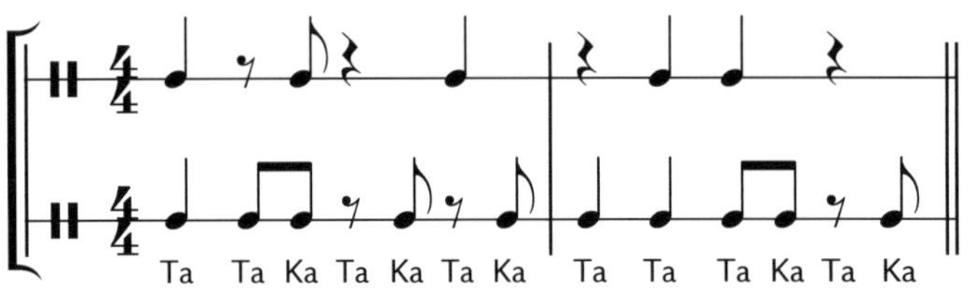

Ex. 11 below is the *2-3 clave* with the *Cáscara* pattern. Practice should be similar to Ex. 10 above.

Ex. 11

Konokol symbols for the above example have been covered in previous examples. The next step is to count the above exercises (4/4) in 2/2 time.

Chapter 1 introduces rhythms which will give the student accurate eighth note timing. The exercises above are based on common Latin music patterns so they have a two-fold use. Students should always play examples on their instrument and challenge themselves to make up their own exercises or compositions using the information given. These should be thoroughly learned before moving on. The exercises should be practised in 4/4 and 2/2 time signatures. All exercises in this book should be repeated to help internalise the patterns.

Chapter 2

Syllabic Counting: Indian Rhythmic Syllables (Konokol)

I will deal with odd metre time signatures in the next chapters, for example, 5/8, 7/8, 9/8, 11/8, and will show examples of how to play a standard song in an odd metre. In chapter 20 original compositions are used to demonstrate odd metre writing, metric modulation and subdivision.

The first step to acquire good odd metre fluency is to practise counting odd-metres using rhythmic syllables. The basic *Konokol* rhythmic system (Indian rhythmic syllabic system), which emulates drum sounds, is very useful. The following basic system is used in this book:

Ta represents a single beat symbol as suggested by the denominator of a time signature.

Ex. 12

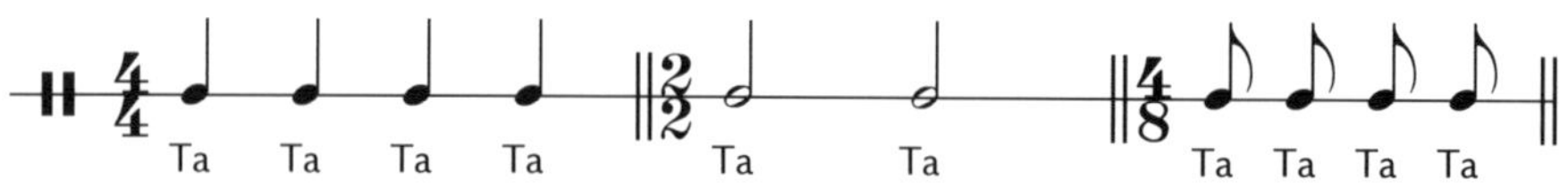

Ta-Ka represents a division of the beat into half.

Ex. 13

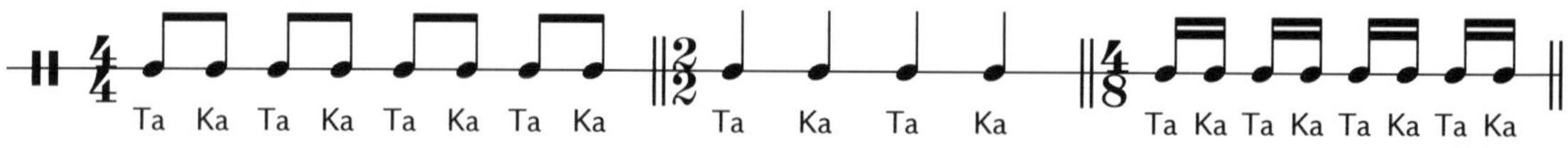

Ta-Ki-Ta represents a division of the beat into three.

Ex. 14

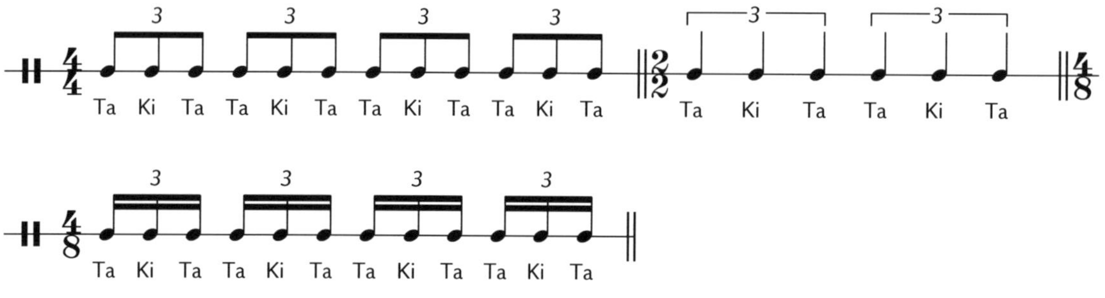

Ta-Ka-Di-Mi represents a division of the beat into four.

Ex. 15

Ta-Di-Ga-Na-Thom represents a division of the beat into five. The Indian syllable *Gi* is substituted by *Ga* in this book.

Ex. 16

For the purposes of this book all other rhythmic groupings are counted by combining the above syllabic groups.

Counting even eighth notes in groups of three

Odd metre is commonly in a time signature which has a denominator 4 or 8, for example, 5/4, 7/4, 9/4, 11/4, 13/4, 5/8, 7/8, 9/8, 11/8, 13/8, 15/8. To count a time signature in 11/8, it is practical to subdivide the bar into smaller groups, for example, 2-2-2-2-3. The first important exercise is to count even eighth notes in groups of three (not triplets). We are used to counting eighth notes in groups of twos and fours, but not even eighth notes in groups of twos and threes.

I will subdivide the four beats in the time signature 4/4 into eighth notes which will be shown as 8/8. 8/8 can be broken into four groups of two eighth notes (normal practice) and combinations of two groups of three plus one group of two: 2-2-2-2, 3-3-2, 3-2-3 or 2-3-3. These groupings can give an effect of performing in an odd metre.

The first exercise is to count 8/8 in the groupings of threes or twos given above using the appropriate *Konokol* syllables. Use these syllables for all the following exercises in this book unless otherwise stated.

Set a metronome at 160 bpm representing eighth notes, and count bar 1 in Ex. 17 below. Remember eighth notes are at a constant tempo, and accents change depending on the subdivided groupings. Tap the eighth notes lightly while emphasizing the accented beats.

3

Ex. 17

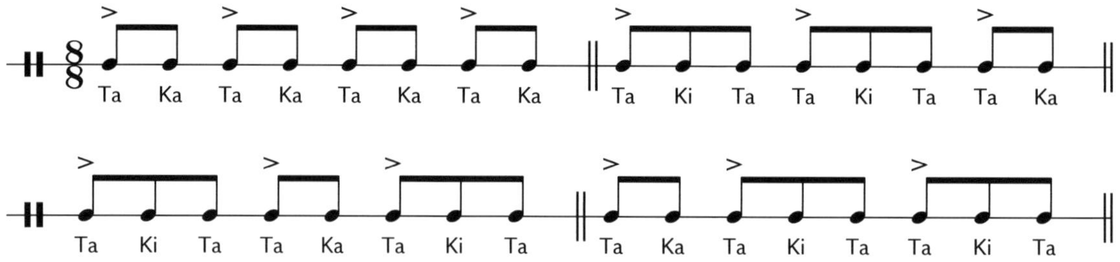

When you are comfortable with the above exercise set a metronome at half speed (80 bpm) and tap four quarter notes per bar while speaking the syllables; eighth notes remain at the same speed. See Ex. 18 below:

4

Ex. 18

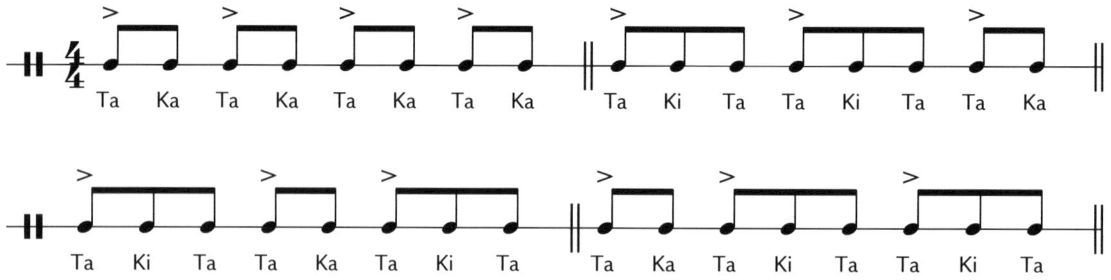

Bar 2 above has an accent on the first eighth note, fourth eighth note and seventh eighth note; this subdivision is similar to a tango rhythm. In bar 3 the accented notes are on eighth notes one, four and six, and in bar 4 on one, three and six. These groupings give interesting rhythmic patterns and prepare you for odd metre playing.

The Konokol syllables really help with rhythmic accuracy. Eighth notes should be counted with a metronome beating eighth notes and at half speed beating quarter notes, as this will give more freedom when counting odd metres.

Chapter 3

Starting Odd Metre: 5 Beats Per Bar

The 5/8 time signature below in Ex. 19 is subdivided into 3-2 and 2-3.

Ex. 19

5

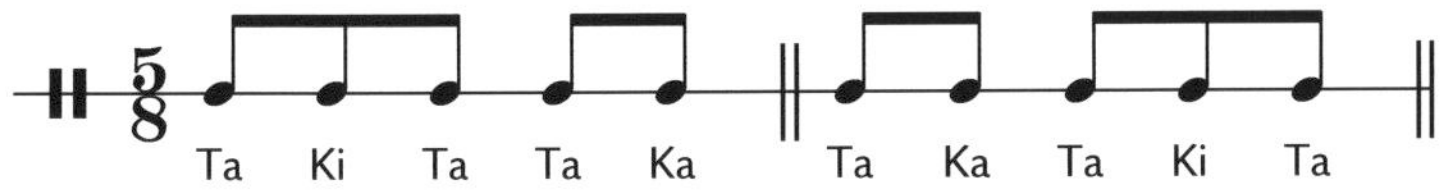

In the first bar above there is an accent on the first eighth note and fourth eighth note. Bar 2 is the opposite to bar 1. Practise the above example while speaking the *Konokol* syllables and emphasize the first beat of each subdivision. Set a metronome at 240 bpm.

Dave Brubeck's *Take Five* is in a medium tempo with a 5/4 time signature, and is written with three strong beats and then two strong beats (equal to a bar of 3/4 and a bar of 2/4 combined), which makes the song rhythmically predictable because of the familiarity of both time signatures. The song feels like it is in extended 3/4 time. It is a great song to learn your basic five-beat time signature.

Set a metronome at 130 bpm. The syllables for bar 1 represent quarter notes; bar 1 can also be counted using the syllables: *Ta-Ta-Ta-Ta-Ta* as shown in brackets.

The *Take Five* rhythmic grouping is shown in bar 3 below.

Ex. 20

6

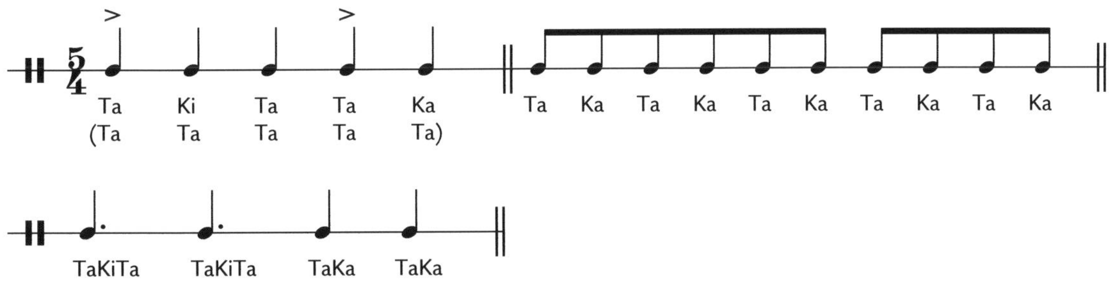

For bar 3 above the division is eighth notes. To find the tempo of the eighth notes, subdivide the beat in the first bar into eighth notes: 2-2-2-2-2 as shown in bar 2. The first three quarter beats of bar 3 are broken into two dotted quarter notes (two beats in the space of three). The bar is an eighth note subdivision of 3-3-2-2.

Because of the familiarity of Take Five *and the predictability of the melodic rhythm, the song is a great first step for odd metre learning.*

CHAPTER 4

Compound Time and Polymetre

Compound time signatures are polymetric, comprising two distinct metres. When you multiply in simple time, the numerator by three and the denominator by two, a compound time signature is created. For example, the corresponding compound time of 2/4 is 6/8; both time signatures have two beats. In simple time, beat and pulse amount to the same, but in compound time they are different. 6/8 has two beats comprising two dotted quarter notes (3 eighth notes in each beat), and a pulse of six eighth notes. When performing in a 2:6 or 6:2 relationship, as shown in bar 2 below, a metric modulation takes place. An Irish jig is a good example of 6/8 time where both beat and pulse feature strongly.

Counting two triplets in 2/4 time, as shown in bar 3 below, will have the same effect as counting six eighth notes in 6/8, provided that the tempo of the beat is similar, but it is rhythmically more complex because the beat is divided into three.

Ex. 21

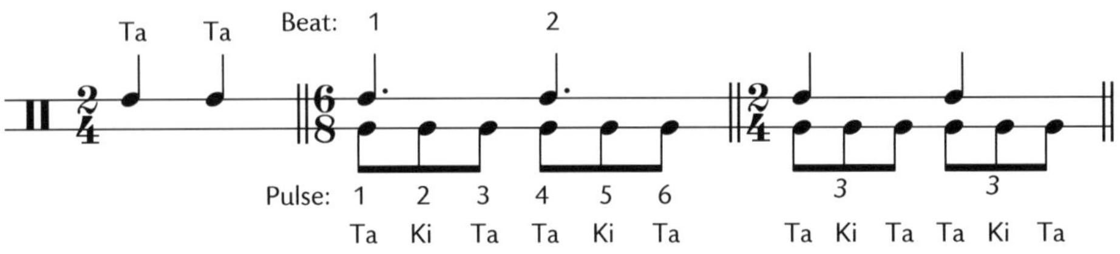

12/8 is common in slow blues songs and is the corresponding compound time of 4/4. A slow blues song in 4/4 time will need more rhythmic interest because of the very slow 4/4 tempo, therefore the song will be performed in 12/8, giving a beat of four and a pulse of 12. See Ex. 22 below.

Ex. 22

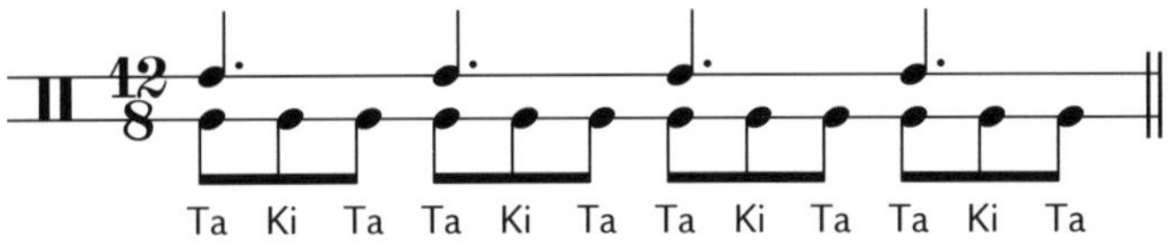

9/8 below is the corresponding compound time signature of the simple time signature 3/4 and is classed as an odd metre.

Ex. 23

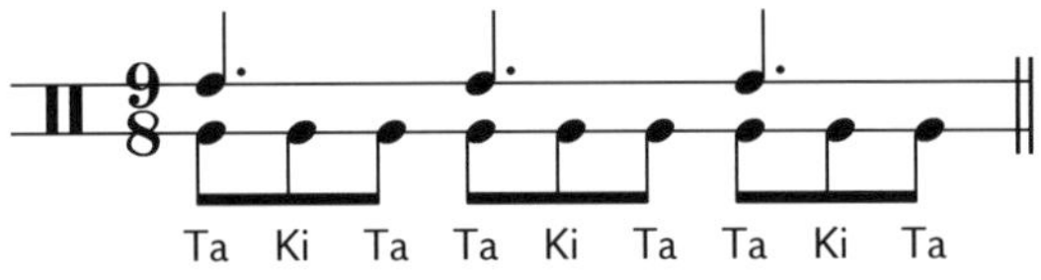

Listen to music which features the time signatures mentioned above, for example A Journey *in chapter 20, p. 50.*

Chapter 5

Metric Modulation in Familiar Time Signatures

Metric modulation is the even mathematical division of a bar or part of a bar in a time signature where the resultant modulation is at a faster or slower tempo. The following examples show essential metric modulations of a bar in common time signatures.

Ex. 24

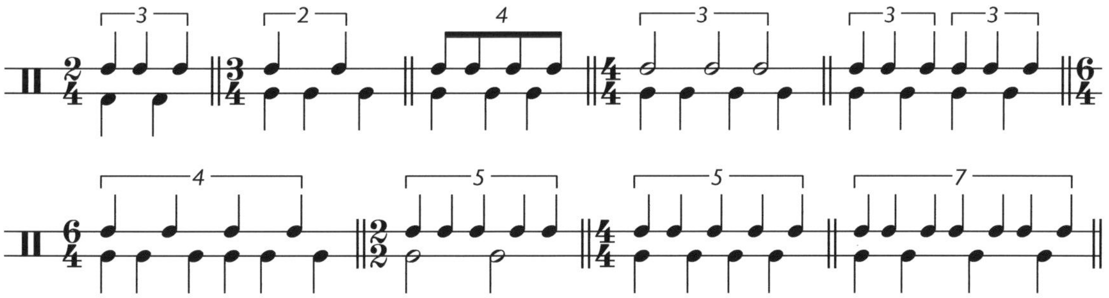

It is important to learn the examples of metric modulation in Ex. 24 above. They are not in order of difficulty and can be broken into a single rhythmic figure for practice as described in chapter 6.

To find the relationship of the modulation to the time signature, find the common denominator by multiplying the bottom number of beats by the number of beats on top. For example, in bar 1 above, multiplying two by three gives a common denominator of six. Each beat must be divided into a triplet – giving six beats. The common denominator of six is the same for bar 2 except that you are creating two equal beats in the space of three beats; therefore the beat is divided into two eighth notes – giving six beats.

Ex. 25 below shows the process of finding a 3:2 (2/4) metric modulation shown in bar 1 above:

Ex. 25

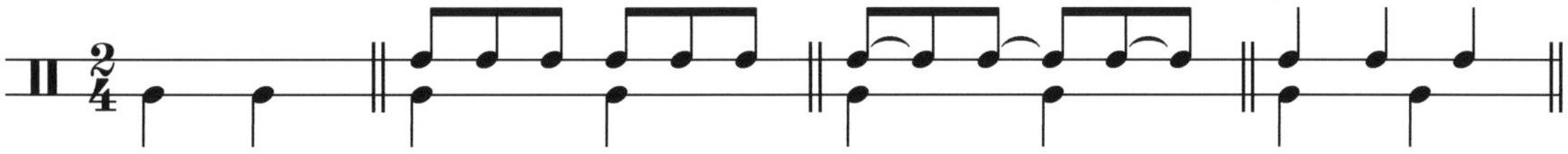

The following example shows the process of finding a 2:3 (3/4) modulation. In bar 2 of Ex. 26 below, the resultant division is simple because the common denominator six is divided by three, equalling two.

Ex. 26

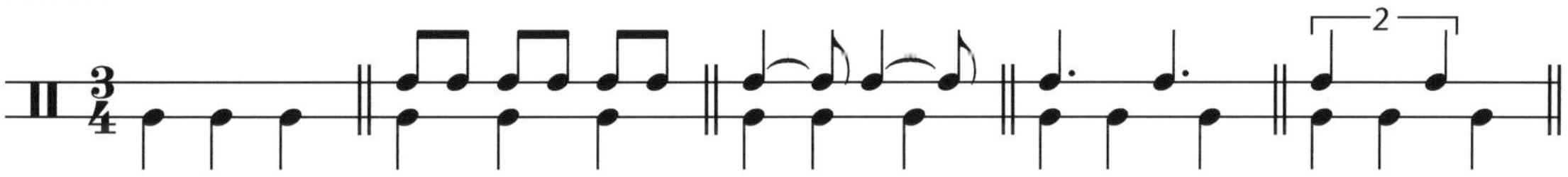

It is less difficult to devise two beats in 3/4 time than three beats in 2/4 time. Practise the above examples; pay attention to detail and do not rush. The examples must be internalized before it becomes natural. Again try and be creative with the information given.

Chapter 6

Reduction Rhythms (Eighth Notes and Triplets) and the Ratios 2:3 (3/4) and 3:2 (2/4)

The following metric modulations go through a reduction process, until a single rhythm is reached which defines each modulation. By accenting different parts of the reduction rhythm the two modulations will become evident when tapped with both hands. When a single reduction rhythm is internalised, use both hands and tap on different sounding surfaces to separate aurally the two rhythms.

Remember whatever time signature you are dealing with when practising a single rhythm reduction with both hands, one hand will beat the beat-unit of that time while the other will beat the accents. Both hands always tap the first beat of the bar then always tap separate beats. Each example shows the ratio of the two metres at the beginning of the bar.

The next step is to practise counting the time signature and resulting modulations out loud so it becomes easy to switch from one to the other. Notice that the modulation is at a different speed to the time signature tempo, which means the ratio also relates to the tempo of the two metres, as already stated. If 60 bpm is used for the 2/4 time signature then three beats pass at 90 bpm (divide the bpm by 2 and multiply the result by 3).

The following example shows the process of reduction, resulting in a single rhythm in the final bar. Familiarise yourself with the rhythm, then tap with both hands on the first beat, and then with separate hands for the following beats and accents. For example: *together-right-left-right.* When comfortable with tapping and singing both metres, play bar 1 on your instrument.

Use two metronomes to assist with hearing the rhythms. If you use multiples of forty per beat, set your metronomes at a ratio of 2x40 : 3x40 = 80 : 120 beats per minute. The metronome speeds will be at a ratio of 2:3 and 3:2.

Ex. 27 2:3

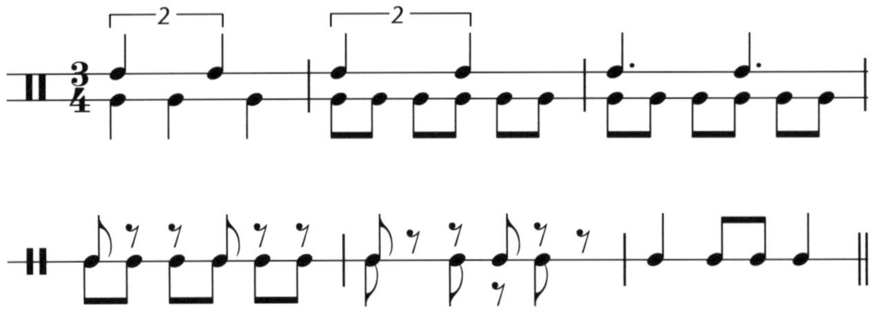

In Ex. 28 below the ratio 3:2 is divided into eighth note triplets and requires the ability to count triplets in various rhythmic combinations. When the single rhythm in bar 5 is internalised, play and sing the written notes in bar 1.

Ex. 28 3:2

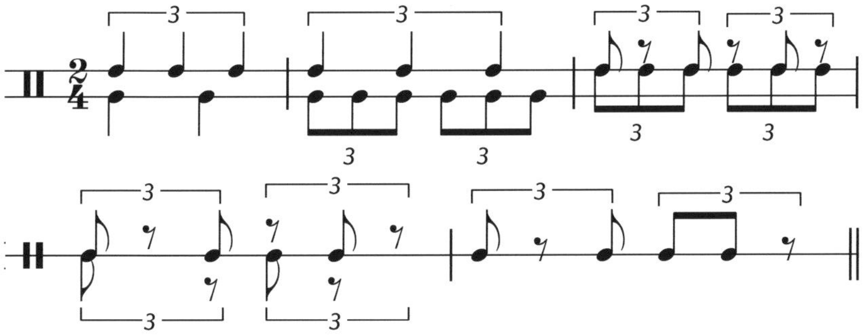

The next step is to count out loud the beat and the resultant modulation above. It should become easy with practice to switch from counting three to counting two without stopping.

For the ratios 3:2 and 2:3 below in Ex. 29 use the syllables *Da* and *Gu* (because there is a distinct change in sound between the two syllables) to highlight the time signature and the modulation. The syllables work well for the other modulations also. For reasons of simplicity the reduction rhythm for 2:3 is used to illustrate both 3:2 and 2:3. In bar 1 the syllable *Da* highlights a three-beat modulation, and in bar 2 a two-beat modulation. Speak the syllables and clap on *Da* in each case. Then use separate hands. Bar 1: *together-right-left-right* and bar 2: *together-left-right-left* while accenting the *Da*. Both modulations will appear in the right hand. Set a metronome at 80 bpm.

Ex. 29 2:3

7

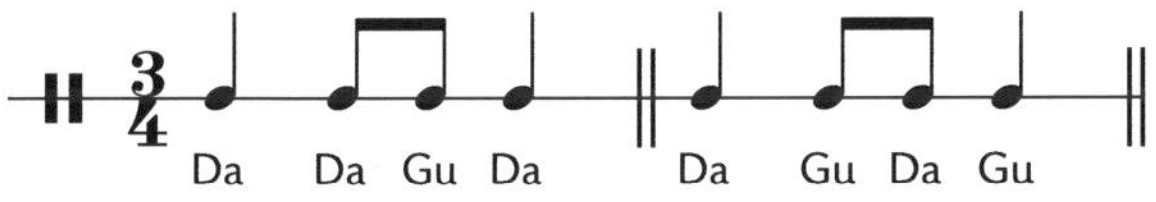

Ex. 30 below shows both reduction rhythms for 2:3 (3/4) and 3:2 (2/4) with *Konokol* syllables. Repeat each one until familiar. Set a metronome at 60 bpm. As in Ex. 29 above use separate hands to beat the rhythm. In this case tap *together-right-left-right* for bar 1 and *together-left-right-left* for bar 2. Notice that the down beat of each bar is tapped by the right hand and the tempo of bar 2 is in a ratio of 3:2.

Ex. 30 2:3

8

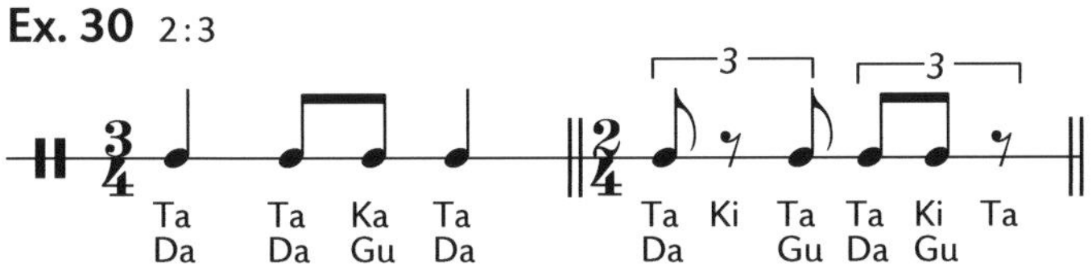

Practise the musical examples below. Set your metronome at 70 bpm. It is important that you are able to highlight the appropriate time signature.

Musical Examples

9

Ex. 31 2:3

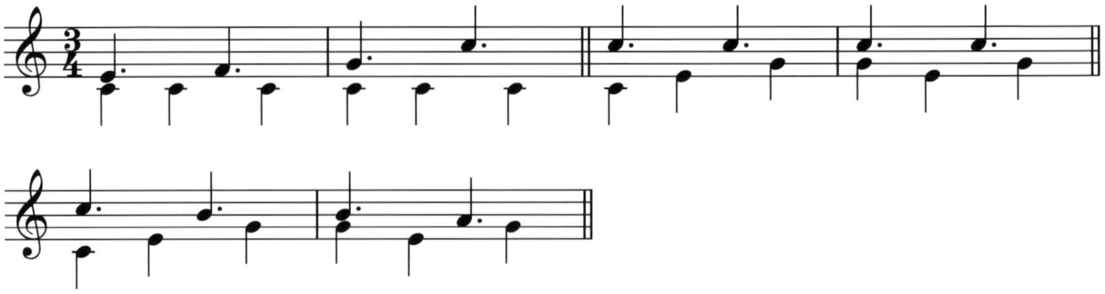

10

Ex. 32 3:2

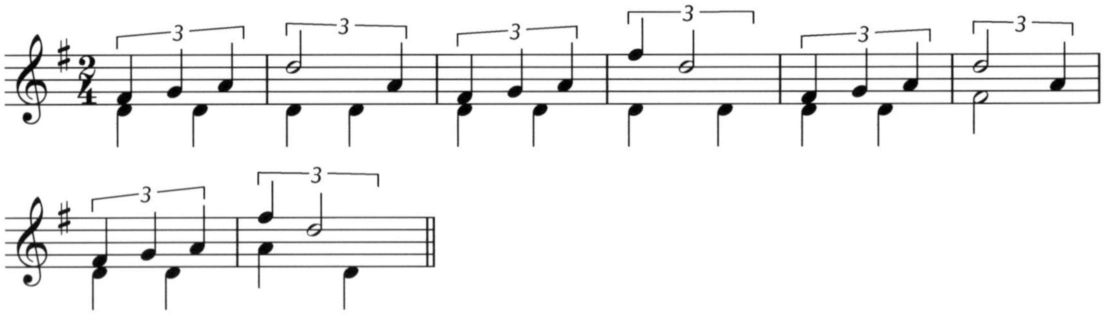

Reduction rhythms are essential tools for understanding the relationship of two metres and for executing the rhythms accurately.

Chapter 7

Reduction Rhythms (Sixteenth Notes and Triplets) and the Ratios 4:3 (3/4), 3:4 (4/4), 6:4 (4/4) and 4:6 (6/4)

The following Ex. 33 below is in ratio 4:3 and shows the process of deducting the reduction rhythm. The common denominator is 4x3 = 12. 12 divided by 3 equals 4. The beat is broken into sixteenth notes to establish four equal subdivisions; divide 12 by 4 = 3, giving four groups of three sixteenth notes. Follow the reduction process and tapping exercises stated in chapter 6, tap the single rhythm in the last bar of Ex. 33 below with one hand first and then with separate hands: *together-right-left-right-left-right.*

The left hand is beating three while the right is beating four. When internalised, play the written notes in bar 1 below. Set your two tempos using multiples of, for example, 20 bpm, which will generate speeds of 80 bpm and 60 bpm, one for modulation and one for the 3/4 beat speed. You will hear the 4:3 (and 3:4) modulation ratio. Initially use the syllables *Da* for the time signature beats and *Gu* for the accented beats.

Ex. 33 4:3

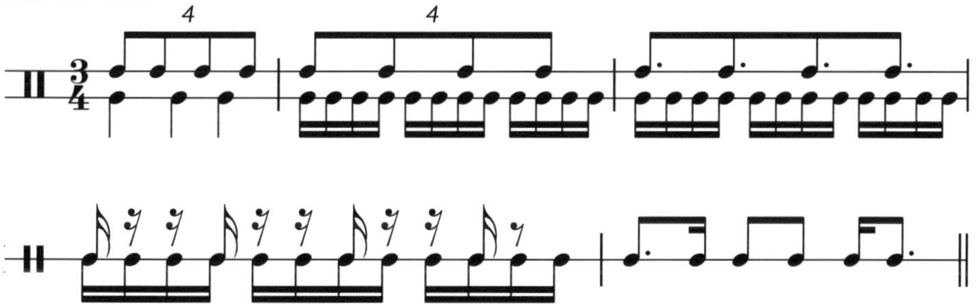

The following metric modulation is triplet based and follows the previous reduction processes.

Ex. 34 3:4

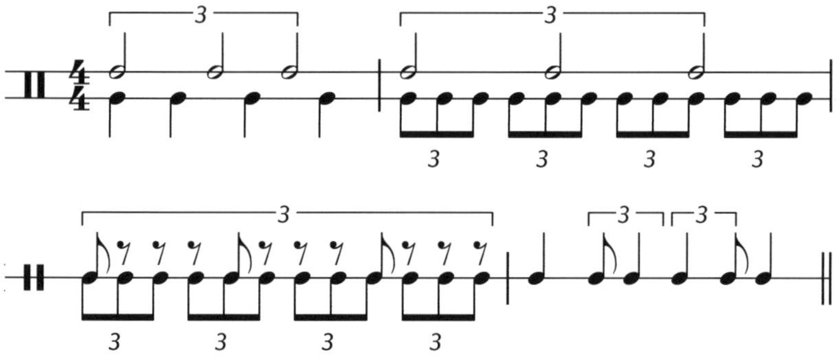

Syllables for the 3:4 ratio are shown in bar 1 of Ex. 35 below, and the 4:3 ratio in bar 2. Both are based on the 4:3 reduction rhythm for reasons of simplicity. Remember the tempo is also in ratio of 3:4 and 4:3. By accenting the *Da* syllables in bar 2, a similar modulation is achieved to the reduction rhythm in the final bar of Ex. 34 above. This is due to the tempo difference of the modulation and time signature as shown in Ex. 35 below. Set a metronome at 80 bpm and speak the syllables in the following exercise. Clap on *Da* in both bars.

11

Ex. 35 4:3

The following example shows both reduction rhythms using *Konokol* syllables. Repeat each one until familiar then play as written. Tap both time signatures with the right hand, bar 1: *together-left-right-left-right-left* and bar 2: *together-right-left-right-left-right.* When comfortable with each bar and syllables set a metronome at 80 bpm. Notice that the down beat of each bar is tapped by the right hand and the tempo in bar 2 is in a ratio 3:4.

12

Ex. 36 4:3

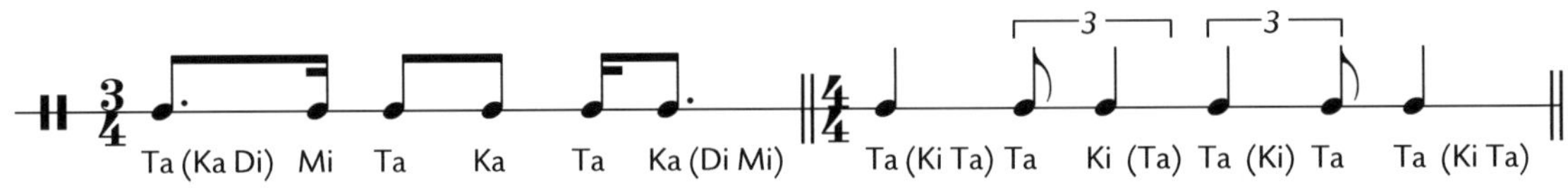

The following Ex. 37 and Ex. 38 show musical examples of 4:3 and 3:4. Set your metronome at 80 bpm. The quadruplet in Ex. 37 below can also be written as four dotted eighth notes. Speak the syllables *Da* and *Gu* for accuracy in performance.

Musical examples

13

Ex. 37 4:3

14

Ex. 38 3:4

Metric Modulations 6:4 (4/4) and 4:6 (6/4)

The following metric modulation is really 3:2 twice in a bar of 4/4, 6:4 subdivided into two groups of 3:2. 4:6 is twice 2:3. The reduction rhythm in the last bar of Ex. 39 below shows syllables for achieving both modulations.

Ex. 39 6:4

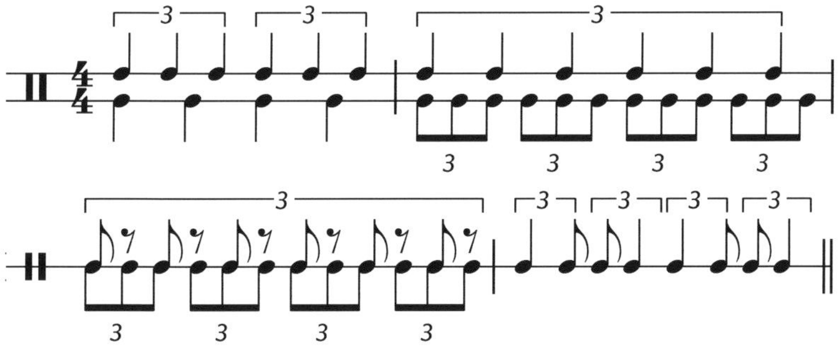

Ex. 40 4:6

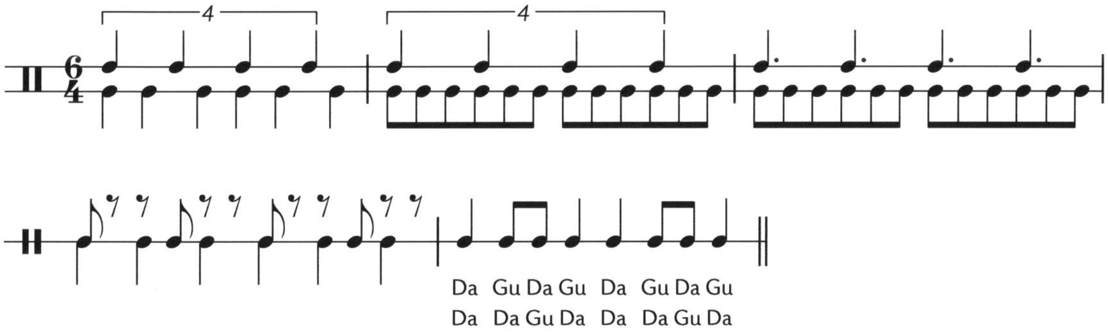

The following example illustrates both reductions rhythms; practise as in previous examples above. For bar 1 tap: *together-right-left-right,* twice and for bar 2: *together-left-right-left*, twice. Set a metronome at 80 bpm. The tempo in bar 2 is in a ratio of 4:6. As in Ex. 36, above the down beat of each bar is tapped by the right hand. The tempo in bar 2 of Ex. 41 below, is in a ratio 6:4.

Ex. 41

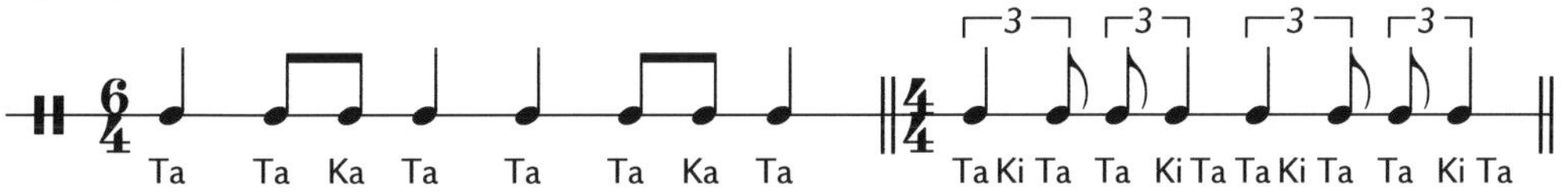

15

The reduction rhythms are essential tools for developing accurate polymetric time sense.

Chapter 8

Odd Metre Time Signatures

The following is a list of odd metre time signatures which will be discussed in the following chapters.

Ex. 42

(a) 5/8, (b) 5/4, (c) 7/8, (d) 7/4, (e) 9/8, (f) 9/4, (g) 10/8, (h) 11/8 (i) 13/8 (j) 15/8

Ex. 43 below contains the half-time time signatures of the above.

Ex. 43

(a) 2½/4, (b) 2½/2, (c) 3½/4, (d) 3½/2, (e) 4½/4, (f) 4½/2, (g) 5/4, (h) 5½/4 (i) 6½/4 (j) 7½/4

It is important to use the knowledge of subdivision given in previous chapters. Let us look at 5/4 and 5/8, and the possibilities of counting and subdividing within these metres.

Subdivision in 5/4 and 5/8

The five-beat time signature was considered briefly in chapter 3. There are many possibilities for dividing 5/4; the common ones are shown in Ex. 44 below. The accents suggest different metric modulations within the metre. Bar 9 suggests 2:5, bar 12 suggests 3:5, and bar 14 suggests 4:5. The following ways to count in 5/4 are shown in Ex. 44 below:

Ex. 44

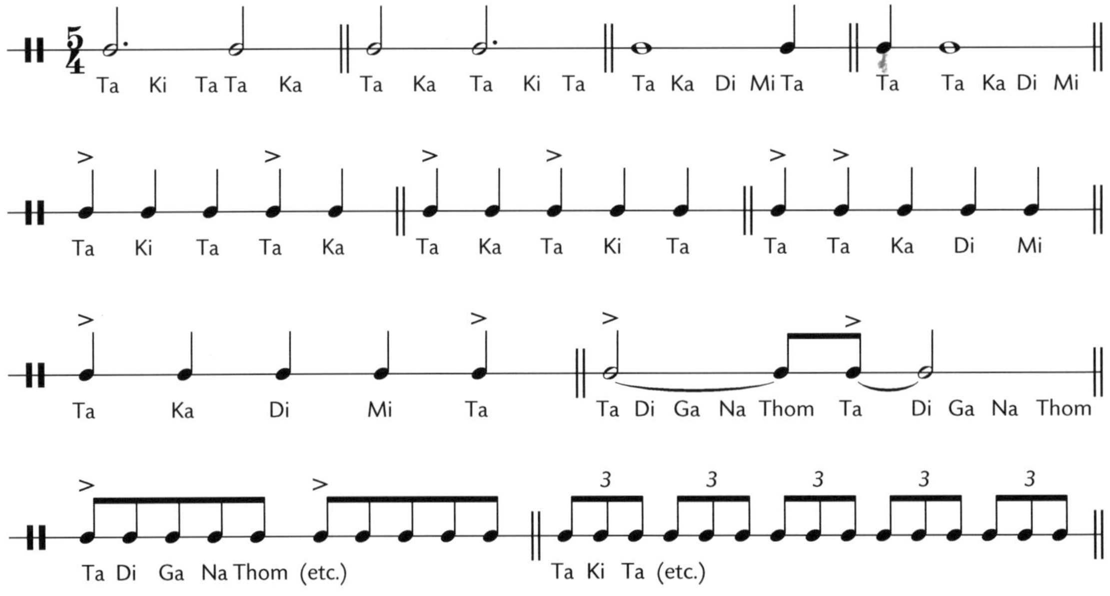

In the above example, I have shown some different ways of subdividing a bar of 5/4. Speak the *Konokol* syllables for clarity of rhythm while tapping on the accents.

The following musical examples are based on bars 5-8 of Ex. 44 above. Chapters 9, 10 and 11 deal with metric modulation and reduction rhythms found in bars 9, 10, 11 and 14 above. Set a metronome at 160 bpm for the next three examples.

Musical Examples

Ex. 45

16

Ex. 46

17

Ex. 47

18

Spend time learning the above information. Remember it is extremely important to learn every piece of information given, as it will assist you when learning the other odd metre time signatures.

CHAPTER 9

Metric Modulation and Reduction Rhythms (Sixteenth Notes and Triplets in Groups of Five) in 5/4 and 5/8

A reduction rhythm can be used for bars 9, 10, 12 and 14 in Ex. 44 above. For bars 9–10 (2:5) see Ex. 48; for bar 12 (3:5) see Ex. 49; and for bar 14 (4:5) see Ex. 50. The first bar of exercises 48, 49 and 50 below are counted with the *Konokol* syllable grouping for five, *Ta-Di-Ga-Na-Thom*. Clap the down beats and speak the syllables. The second bar of Ex. 50 shows the reduction rhythm for 4:5. The syllables underneath bar 2 are for the modulations 4:5 and 5:4 and should be practised similar to previous reduction rhythms.

Ex. 48 2:5

Ex. 49 3:5

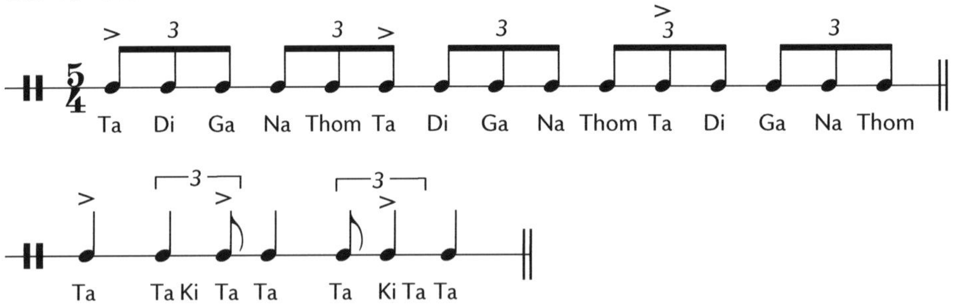

Ex. 50 4:5

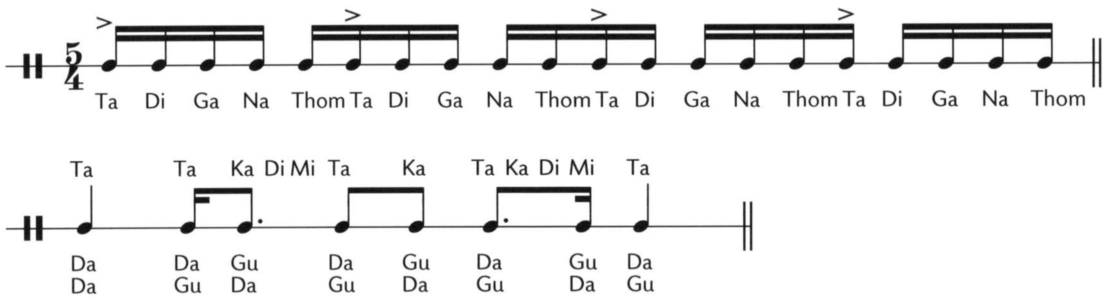

Musical Examples

The following musical examples, Ex. 51 and Ex. 52, illustrate simple lines for bars 11–16 in Ex. 44, chapter 8.

Set a metronome at 80 bpm. In bars 2 and 4 the example highlights the ratios 3:5 and 4:5 respectively. Practise bar 1 first to get the feeling for the triplet speed, speaking the *Konokol* syllables for a group of three, then play and speak the syllables for a group of five in bar 2 (three groups).

The next step is to speak the syllables for three while playing the second bar. For bars 3 and 4 below, play the example in bar 3 to find the tempo of the sixteenth notes and count the *Konokol* syllables for a group of four, then play bar 4 and speak the syllables for a group of five (four groups).

The next step is to play bar 4 while counting the syllables for a group of four.

Ex. 51

19

In Ex. 52 below, bars 2, 4 and 6 highlight 3:5 and 4:5, using a melodic/scalar pattern. Count the *Konokol* syllables similar to Ex. 51 above.

Ex. 52

20

In the following example the time signature is 5/8. The musical examples above can be transferred to 5/8.

Set a metronome at 130 bpm. Practise bars 1 to 10 inclusive using this method. At this point the material in chapter 1, which stated the importance of the up beat as well as the down beat, comes into play. In bar 9 the beat is subdivided into half (sixteenth notes). Practise bars 11 to 14 of Ex. 53 below at 90 bpm. Track 21 on the CD features bars 1 to 10, track 22 shows bars 11–14. Each bar is clapped (and spoken) twice.

Ex. 53

21

22

The information in this chapter is very important. When learned properly the information in the following chapters will be easier to understand.

Chapter 10

Metric Modulation, Reduction Rhythms (Quintuplets) and the Ratios 5:2 (2/2) and 2:5 (5/4)

The following two exercises are in the ratios 5:2 and 2:5. Odd metres are quite easily divided into two parts; see Ex. 54 below:

Ex. 54 5:2

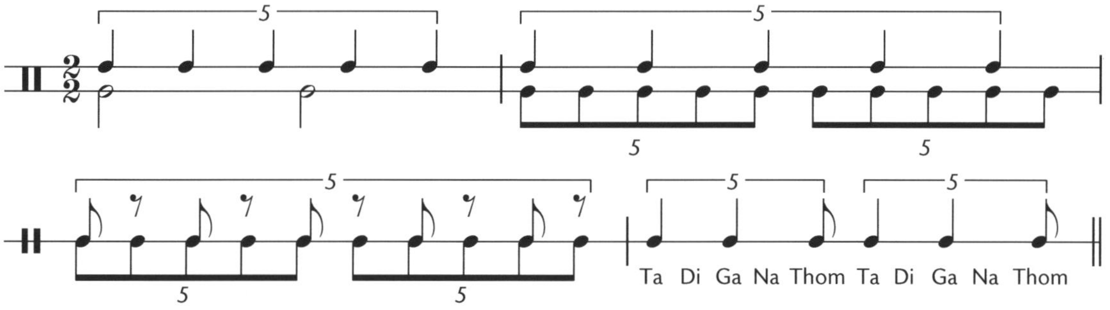

Modulating 5:2 is much more difficult than modulating 2:5 because two beats are divided into quintuplets. The following musical example is the 2:5 reduction rhythm. Set a metronome at 120 bpm.

Musical Example

Ex. 55 2:5

23

Compose your own exercises based on previous musical examples and ideas. It is important to practise counting quintuplets in various rhythmic forms.

Chapter 11

Metric Modulation, Reduction Rhythms (Quintuplets) and the Ratios 5:4 (4/4) and 4:5 (5/4)

The following two examples are the 5:4 (4/4) and 4:5 (5/4) ratios which follow a step-by-step process to finding the reduction rhythms of each ratio. It is important to use the knowledge of metric modulation and subdivision given in previous chapters.

Ex. 56 5:4

Ex. 57 4:5

As with previous examples the second modulation above is much easier than the first. Use the syllables in Ex. 58 below for the 4:5 reduction rhythm. Bar 1 is 4:5 and bar 2 is 5:4. The 4:5 and 5:4 ratios are achieved, like in previous examples, using one reduction rhythm. In bar 2 the syllables switch emphasis and give a similar effect to the devising of five beats in 4/4 time (see Ex. 58, bar 2, below). Set your metronome at 90 bpm and clap on *Da*:

ISBN 9790206309915

24

… four beats must be divided into quintu- …ns 4:5 (5/4), shown in Ex. 58 above, and

…n in bar 1 of Ex. 59 below, then count the …d 4 the beat is divided into four sixteenth …ur in bar 5. The syllables in bar 4 give a … a metronome at 80 bpm on a thirty-one … one, six, eleven, sixteen, twenty, twenty- …es while clapping on each beat.

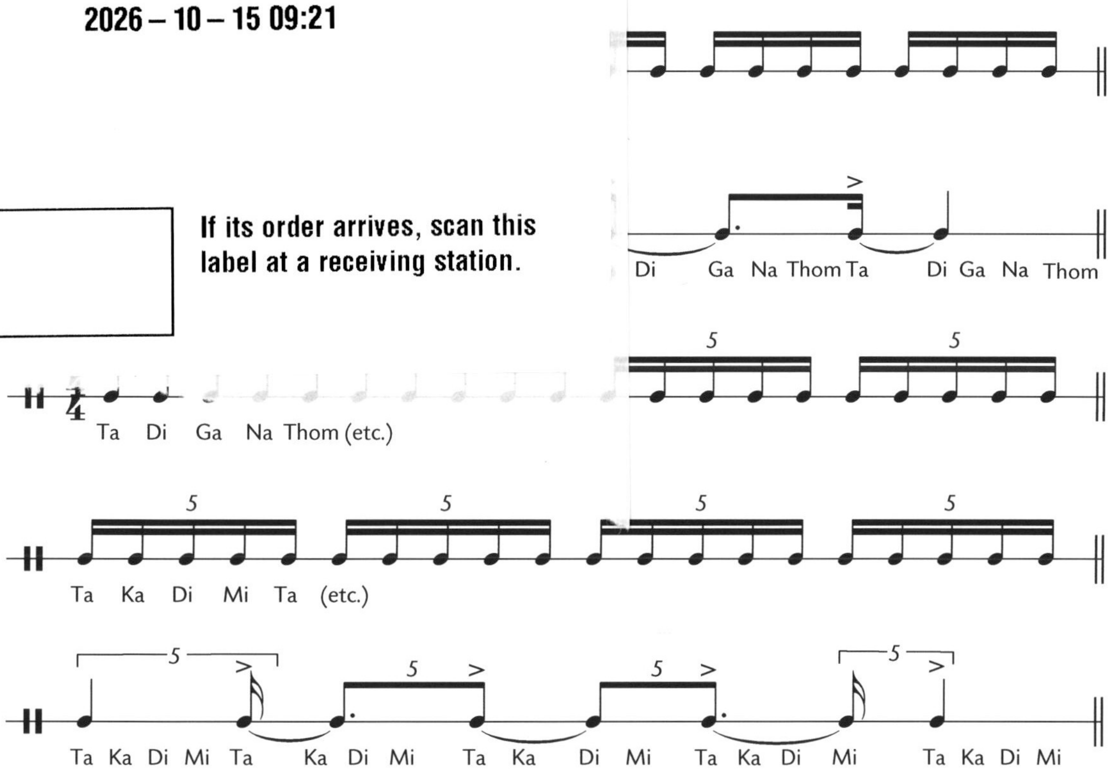

25

Musical Examples

The following musical example has five beats in the lower voice and four in the top voice. Set a metronome at 90 bpm and speak syllables.

Ex. 60 4:5

26

Ex. 61 below illustrates quintuplets in 4/4 time where the melody is subdivided on each beat into: 2½/16 – 2½/16 – 2½/16 – 2½/16 (2-3 – 2-3 – 2-3 – 2-3). Count *Ta-Di-Ga-Na-Thom* for each quintuplet or *TaKi – TaKiTa.* Set your metronome at 60 bpm.

27

Ex. 61 5:4

The following example highlights 5:4 in the melody. The reduction rhythm in Ex. 61 above is very useful here for highlighting both the four beats of the time signature and the five beats of the modulation. The melody is easily memorised which makes the modulation easier to learn. Set a metronome at 80 bpm.

28

Ex. 62 5:4

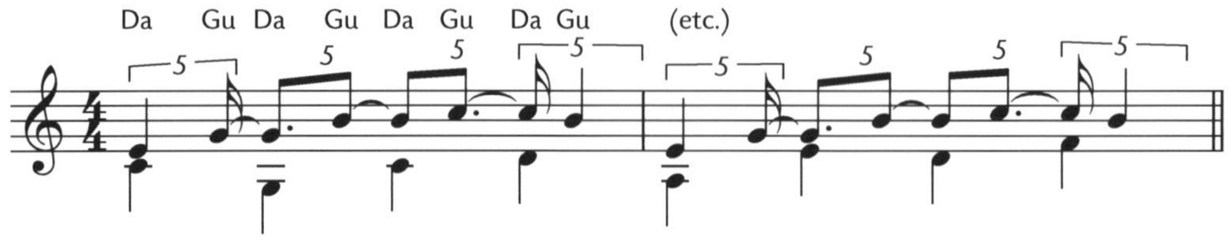

The metric modulations above are challenging. It is important to formulate your own musical examples and ideas.

Chapter 12

Subdivision in 7/4 and 7/8

7/4 and 7/8 time signatures are probably the most commonly used. The only difference between 5/8 and 7/8 is that the numerator is larger by two – two eighth notes or a quarter note more. See the following time signatures and subdivisions and notice the added quarter note change from metre to metre: 5/8 = 2-3, 7/8 = 2-2-3, 9/8 = 2-2-2-3, 11/8 = 2-2-2-2-3, 13/8 = 2-2-2-2-2-3, and so on.

The following exercise is in 7/4 time and illustrates a number of possible ways of counting a bar of seven. The accents in bars 17, 19 and 21 are in a ratio of 2:7, 3:7 and 4:7 respectively. Many kinds of folk music contain a seven-beat cycle similar to bar 11 below, where the subdivision is 3-2-2. The accents on the '3' are commonly on the first and second beats. Utilise the information in chapters 8 and 9 to formulate exercises which should be straightforward at this stage. Practise with your metronome at 120 bpm representing quarter notes.

Ex. 63

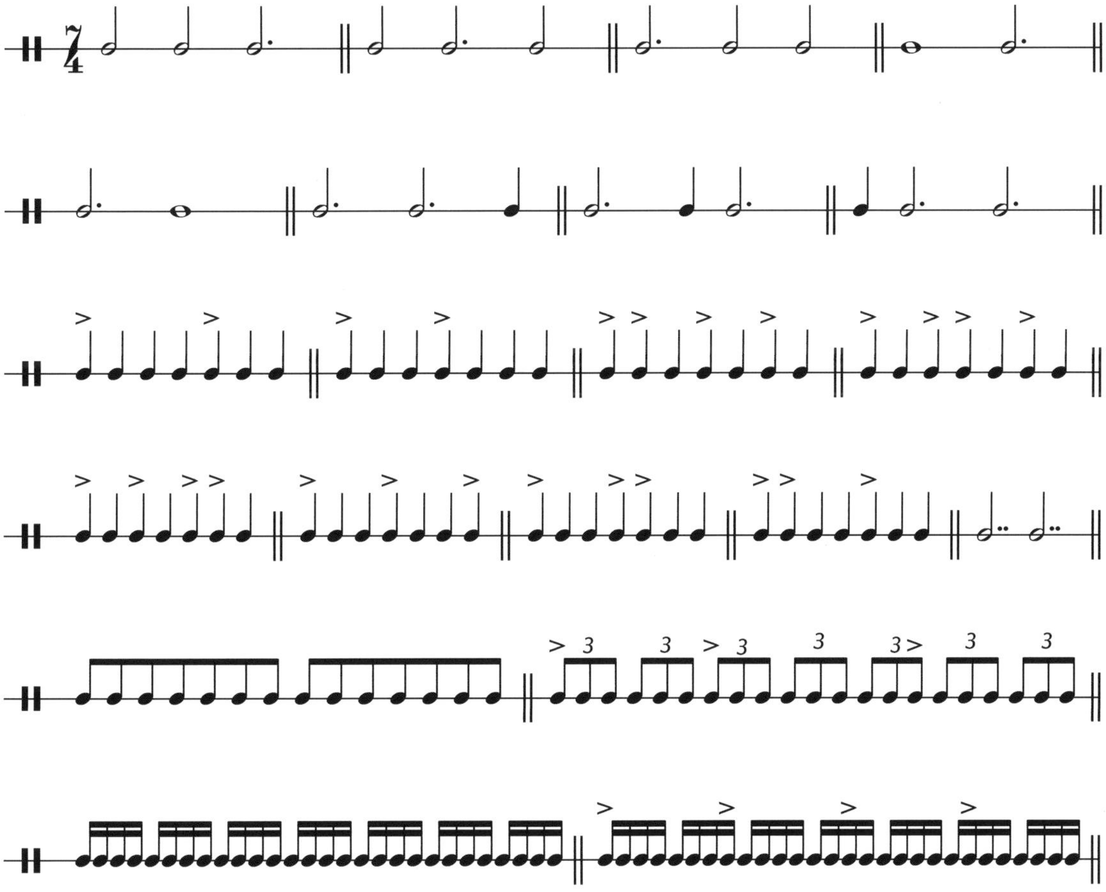

Practise with your metronome set at 120 bpm, representing eighth notes, then with your metronome set at 120 bpm, representing quarter notes. When the metronome beat is on quarter notes the repeat bars in Ex. 64 below will be on the up beat. Remember that bars 17, 18 and 19 suggest metric modulations and will be discussed in chapters 13 and 14.

Ex. 64

Musical Example

Ex. 65 below shows a melody using a 2-2-3 subdivision. Set a metronome at 120 bpm representing quarter notes and count the written *Konokol* syllables. Note that every two bars the melody will start on the first beat of the seven-beat cycle (7/4).

Ex. 65

29

The information learned in previous chapters will assist you when developing exercises for 7/4 and 7/8. All the information is transferable to the other odd metres. There are many jazz artists who have recorded songs in 7/4 or 7/8 so it is essential to research the subject further. See the original compositions African Way and Song For Lieb in chapter 20, pp. 48 and 49.

Chapter 13

Metric Modulation, Reduction Rhythms (Septuplets) and the Ratios 7:2 (2/2) and 2:7 (7/4)

The following example is in a 7:2 metric modulation with the reduction rhythm in the last bar. Because the division is septuplets (common denominator equals 14) it is a difficult modulation to count. The fourth bar is shown as 2-2-3, 3-2-2 and is equivalent to two bars of 3½/4 (7/8). The second septuplet may be counted: *TaKaDiMi – TaKiTa*, like the first septuplet for practice purposes, then as written. When familiar with the seven pulse use the following syllables (the *Ka* in bold marks the half bar) for bar 4: *Ta-Ta-Ta-Ta***Ka***-Ta-Ta-Ta.* The syllables will give the same result as the reduction rhythm in Ex. 67.

Ex. 66 7:2

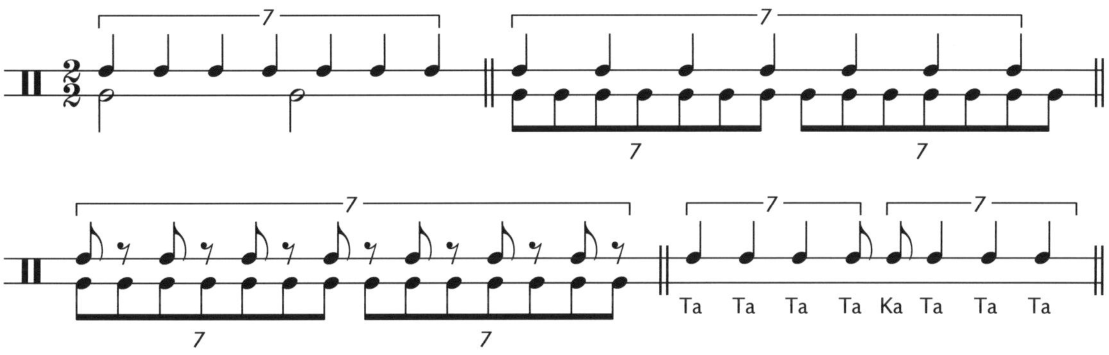

The following modulation 2:7 divides easily. The half bar is on the second eighth note of the fourth beat. The time signature is 7/4. Set your metronome at 120 bpm in 7/4 and tap the reduction rhythm.

Ex. 67 2:7

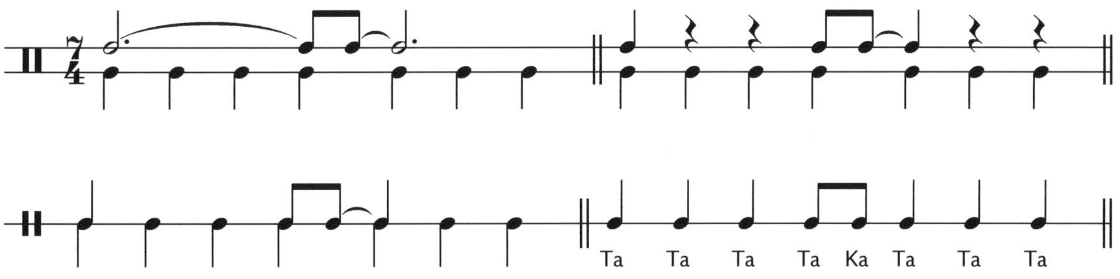

Note: If you remove one quarter note from the beginning and the end (beats one and beats seven) you arrive at the 5:2 reduction rhythm. If you remove two from each side (beats one and two and beats six and seven) you arrive at the 3:2 reduction rhythm.

Musical Examples

For the following musical example set your metronome at 120 bpm.

30

Ex. 68 2:7

Ex. 69 below is a challenge. Set your metronome at 60 bpm and count *TaKa-TaKa-TaKiTa* per click. Then *Ta-Ta-TaKiTa,* and finally *Ta-Ta-Ta-TaKa-Ta-Ta-Ta* where the *Ka* will mark the division of the bar into half.

31

Ex. 69 7:2

7:2 is based on septuplets and presents a challenging exercise. As stated before it is important to formulate your own musical examples and ideas. Subdividing an odd metre into two will give you a familiar platform to work on other modulations.

Chapter 14

Metric Modulation, Reduction Rhythms (Septuplets) and the Ratios 7:4 (4/4) and 4:7 (7/4)

The following examples show the modulation and reduction rhythm of 7:4 (4/4) and 4:7 (7/4). When familiar with the tempo of the septuplet, count the bar 5 in Ex. 70 below and tap the rhythm. Use the syllables written above the notes and tap with both hands on the first beat of the rhythm and then alternate hands for the following subdivisions.

Ex. 70 7:4

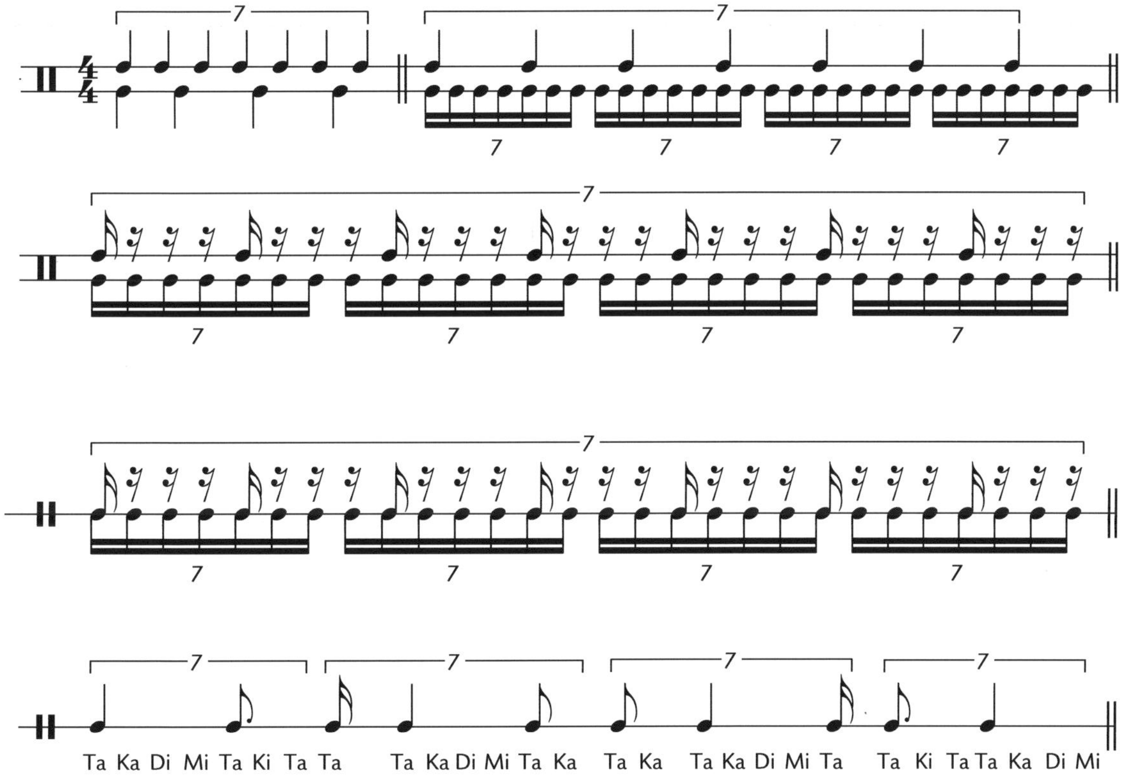

In Ex. 71 below it is best to set your metronome beating sixteenth notes for practice.

Ex. 71 4:7

In Ex. 72 below the 4:7 reduction rhythm is used to demonstrate both the time signature and the modulation. In the first bar the *Da* syllable highlights seven beats and the syllables are reversed in the second bar – *Da* highlights the modulation 4:7. Set your metronome at 130 bpm and clap on *Da* in each bar. Then use separate hands to highlight the modulation as before.

Ex. 72

32

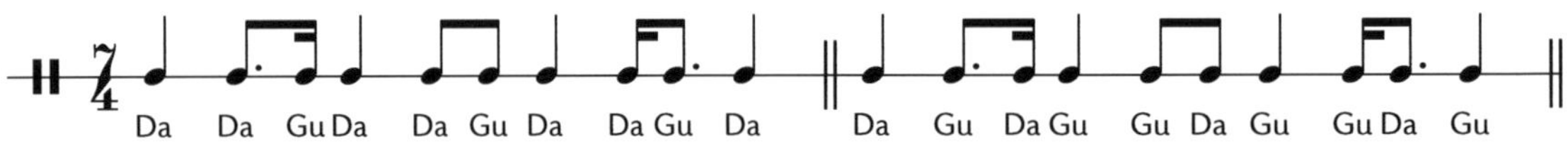

Note: If you remove the four quarter notes in the example above the resulting rhythm is the 4:3 reduction rhythm. If you remove the first two beats and the last two beats the resultant reduction rhythm is 3:2.

The following Ex. 73 below shows both reduction rhythms. The syllables in Ex. 72 above should be used for Ex. 73 below. Alternative syllables for bar 2 are shown in brackets representing septuplet beats. Clap on the first beat of each septuplet. Set a metronome at 80 bpm. The tempo in bar 2 is in a ratio of 7:4. As with previous examples keep the down beat of each metre in the right hand.

Ex. 73

33

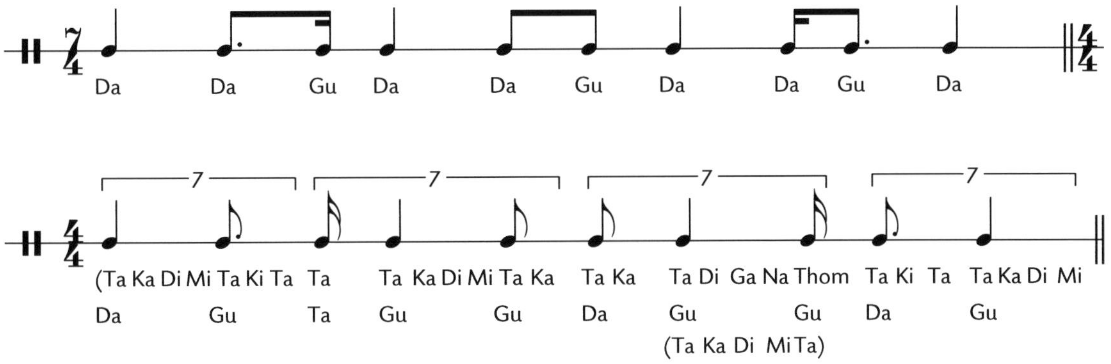

Musical Example

Set your metronome at 100 bpm for Ex. 74 below.

Ex. 74 4:7

34

7:4 is based on septuplets and is a more challenging modulation than 7:2, presented in the previous chapter, because you are dealing with four septuplets. As stated before it is important to formulate your own musical examples and ideas.

CHAPTER 15
Subdivision of the Ratio 10:7 (7/4)

I will give four methods below for devising the metric modulation 10:7, which will enable you to perform the composition *Song For Lieb* (7/4), p. 49, chapter 20.

Method 1:

To find the subdivision of 10:7 the eighth note must be divided into thirty-second note quintuplets. The common denominator is 70 (14 quintuplets), and every seven quintuplet beats will give you ten even beats. Notice that starting on the eighth note of the reduction rhythm in bar 3, the rhythm is a repeat of the previous seven-beat rhythmic figure. So, in fact the reduction rhythm is 5:3½ quarter notes times 2 = 10:7.

For initial practice speak out loud *Ta-Di-Ga-Na-Thom* with a metronome on a five-beat cycle while you tap with separate hands; *Ta-Di, Ta-Ga, Ta-Na* and so on. This will get you used to tapping on different parts of a quintuplet. For Ex. 75 below, set your metronome on a seven-beat cycle at 45 bpm and count bar one while clapping on the down beat. Then count ten times *Ta-Ka-Di-Mi – Ta-Ki-Ta,* as shown in bar 2 while clapping on the first beat of each seven beat subdivision. It is impossible to count this exercise at 180 bpm which is required for *Song For Lieb,* however it is a great exercise to work on quintuplet subdivisions in groups of seven. The rhythmic result of clapping subdivisions of seven against the metronome beat of 45 bpm is shown in bar 3 below. Count on each beat: *Ta-Di-Ga-Na-Thom.* To avoid clutter, only the important syllables are shown (*Ta* always marks the beginning of each quintuplet).

35

Ex. 75 10:7

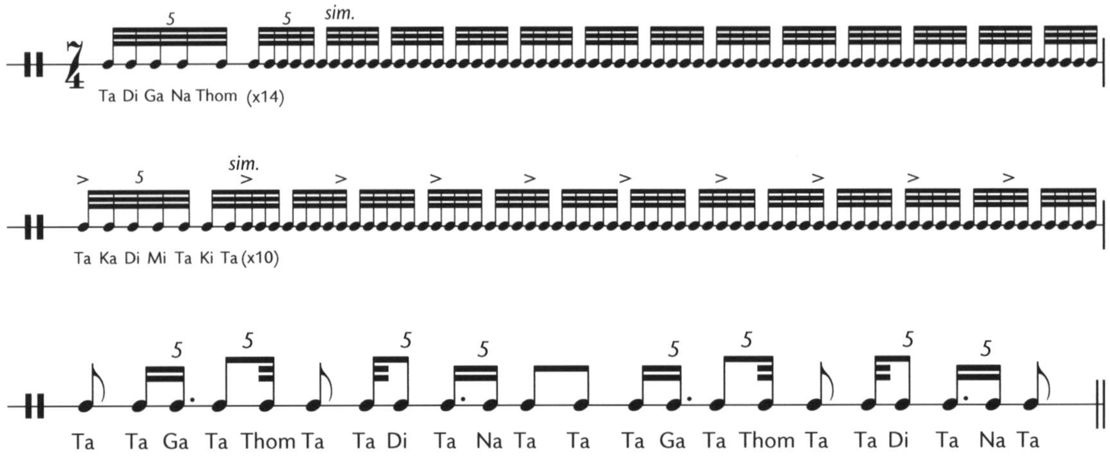

Method 2:

Method 2 is a division of the seven beats into five (every seven quintuplet beats as shown in bar 1, Ex. 76 below). Then the tempo is doubled giving a ratio of 10:7. Set a metronome at 70 bpm and tap seven quintuplets; five quintuplets in groups of seven and then the reduction rhythm in bar 2, Ex. 76 with separate hands. The reduction rhythm is similar to the first seven beats of Method 1 and the syllables are written out in their entirety. Other syllables that can be used to count bar 3 of Ex. 76 below are shown in brackets (syllables repeat twice in bar 2, Ex. 75 above).

Ex. 76 5:7

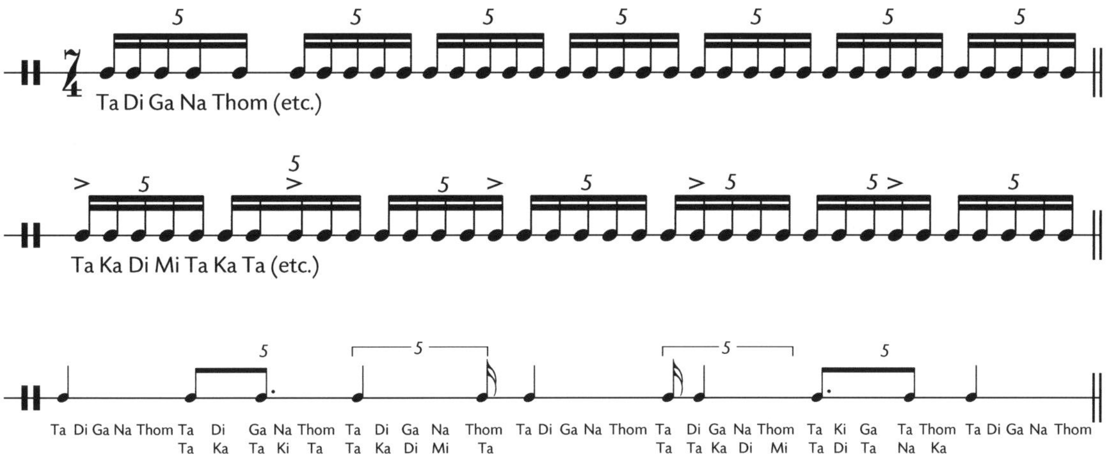

36

Method 3:

Count with a metronome on a seven-beat cycle (count *Ta-Ka-Di-Mi – Ta-Ki-Ta*). Then set the metronome at a seventh of the speed and clap seven beats on each click. For example, clap with the metronome on 280 bpm (140 and an eighth note click for a basic electronic metronome). Secondly set the metronome at 40 bpm (remember the speed of the seven beats); clap on each click while you count the seven beats – the speed should be at 280 bpm – the original metronome speed.

Method 4:

Song For Lieb should be played at a tempo of approximately 180 bpm. Method 4 first divides the 7/4 beat into half. Ex. 77 below illustrates (see chapter 13) seven beats and the division into two, which falls on beat one, and the second eighth note of beat four. Set your metronome at 120 bpm and speak syllables.

Ex. 77

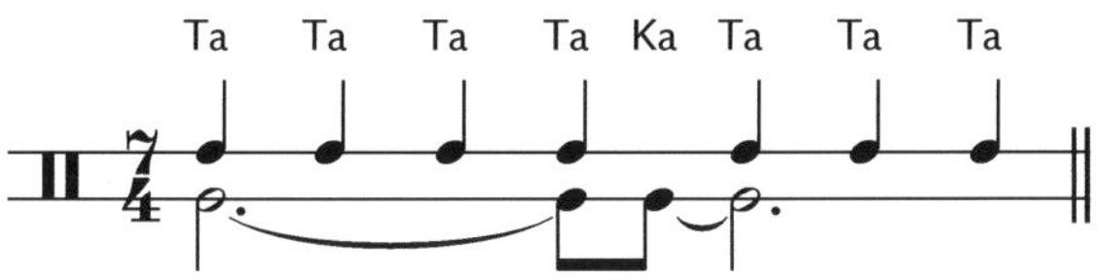

37

This method is more mathematical in approach. Count with a metronome on a five-beat cycle. Then set the metronome at a fifth of the speed and clap five beats on each click. For example, clap with the metronome on 280 bpm (140 bpm and an eighth note click for a basic electronic metronome). Secondly place the metronome on 56 bpm and clap five beats per click; the speed should be at 280 bpm – the original metronome speed. To find seven beats in the same time frame the metronome should be set at 392 bpm (196 bpm and an eighth-note click). This is the speed of seven beats over five beats. When familiar with this tempo, place the metronome on 56 bpm and clap the seven beats per click which should be at a speed of 392 bpm. To find the tempo of ten beats in the same time frame, double the tempo of 56 bpm to 112 bpm and count five beats per click. This method can be very useful if you are finding it difficult to hear or tap the ratio 10:7. Bars 15, 16, 17 and 18 in *Song For Lieb* contain this modulation which is subdivided into 4-2-4 (*Ta-Ka-Di-Mi – Ta-Ka – Ta-Ka-Di-Mi*).

The 10:7 modulation is the final piece of information needed to learn the composition Song For Lieb *p. 49, chapter 20. It is easier to absorb a difficult modulation if a melody is constructed to highlight it.*

CHAPTER 16

Subdivision and Metric Modulation in 9/8

9/8 time can be subdivided into three equal beats; therefore it is different from the other odd metres and has a suggested polymetric rhythm.

Dave Brubeck's *Blue Rondo à la Turk* is a good example of 9/8 broken into 2-2-2-3 and 3-3-3. The rhythm of the song is illustrated in Ex. 78 below. This grouping can be seen as 4½/4 (half time of 9/8). What makes 9/8 a little different is that it is divisible by three, so one can easily modulate to an even three-beat time signature (as shown in bar 4 below). The ratio relationship between the first three beats of bars 1, 2 or 3 and the first two beats of bar 4 is 3:2. These familiar modulations help when modulating to other metres within odd metre music, hence giving interesting rhythmic ideas while performing or composing. Set a metronome at 120 bpm representing quarter notes. Track 38 features bars 1 through 4 of Ex. 78, played twice.

Ex. 78

38

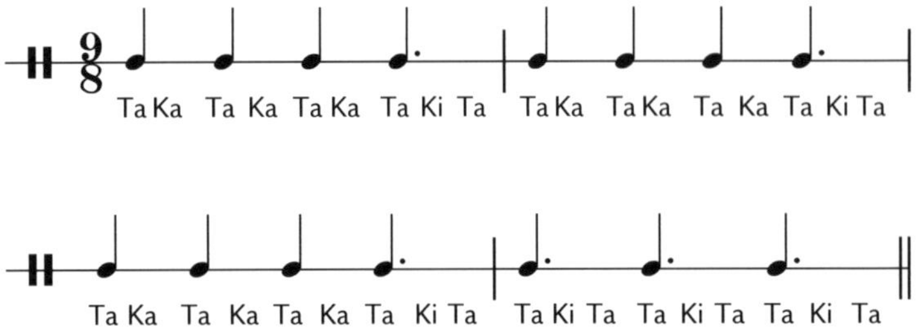

Ex. 79 below illustrates how you can modulate to two even beats. Set a metronome at 70 bpm representing three beats in 9/8. Track 39 features bars 1 through 4 of Ex. 79, played twice, with one bar of introduction (*Ta-Ki-Ta – Ta-Ki-Ta – TaKi-Ta*).

Ex. 79

39

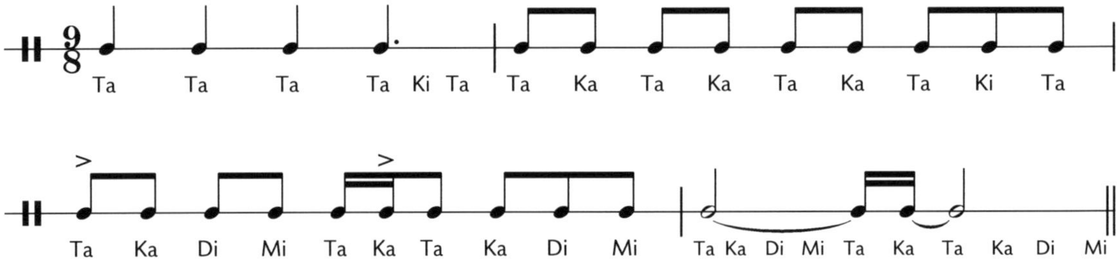

Ex. 80 below illustrates another way of arriving at an even two-beat modulation using the ratio 2:3, in bar 4. The last bar shows four even beats over 9/8 or 4½/4. This is achieved by doubling the tempo of the two beats in bar 5. The opposite is to have a 4:3 modulation in bar 4 and halve the speed of the four beats. It makes for an interesting four-metre modulation of 4½:4:3:2. Your timing must be strong and precise to execute a modulation like this. Set a metronome on a three beat cycle at 80 bpm representing three beats in 9/8, and speak the syllables. In bars 4, 5 and 6 clap on the *Da* syllable. Track 40 features each bar of Ex. 80 played twice, with two introductory bars of the 3-3-3 (*Ta-Ki-Ta*) subdivision.

Ex. 80

40

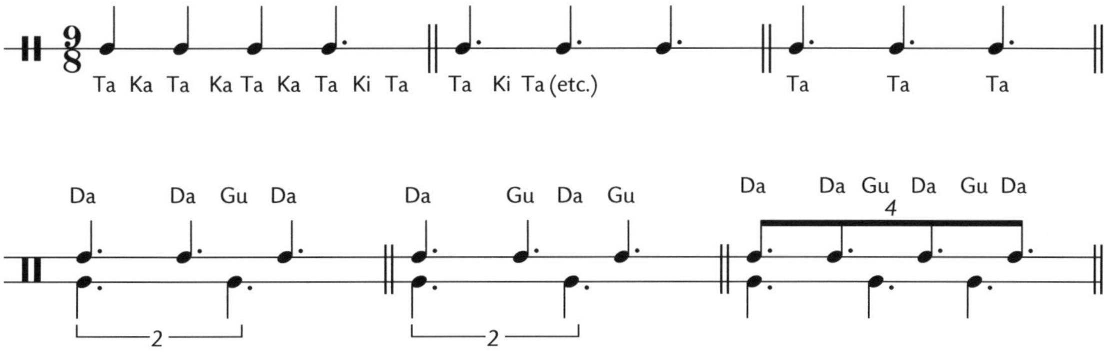

The same result as Ex. 80 above is achieved in Ex. 81 below. The difference is that in bar 3 the time signature is changed to 3/4 (dotted quarter equals a quarter). Set a metronome on a three beat cycle at 80 bpm representing three beats in 9/8, and speak the syllables. Note the two introductory bars of the 3-3-3 subdivision (*Ta-Ki-Ta*), on track 41.

Ex. 81

41

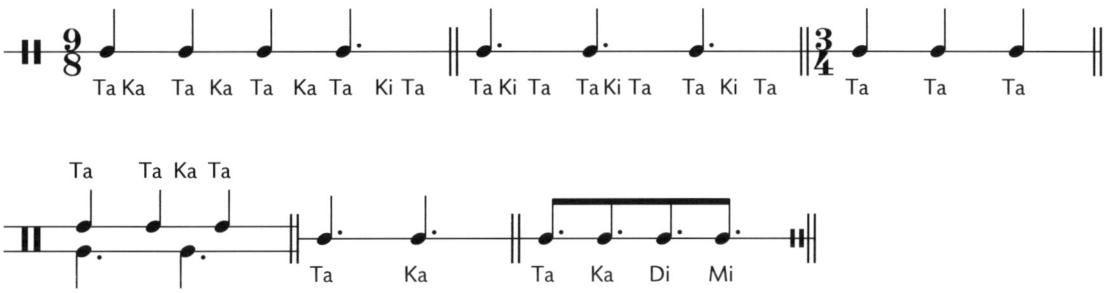

Ex. 82 below illustrates the four-metre modulation of 4½:4:3:2. If the tempo of the 9/8 bar is, for example, 120 bpm, then a quarter note will have a tempo of 60 bpm and a dotted quarter note will have a tempo of 40 bpm. For the other modulation the beat has to be divided into sixteenth notes which have a tempo of 240 bpm. Two beats within 9/8 will have nine/sixteenths each and a tempo of 29⅔ bpm. Four beats will have a tempo double that, which is 53⅓ bpm. This is the type of precision that is needed to perform metric modulation correctly. This is where reduction rhythms are very useful.

Ex. 82

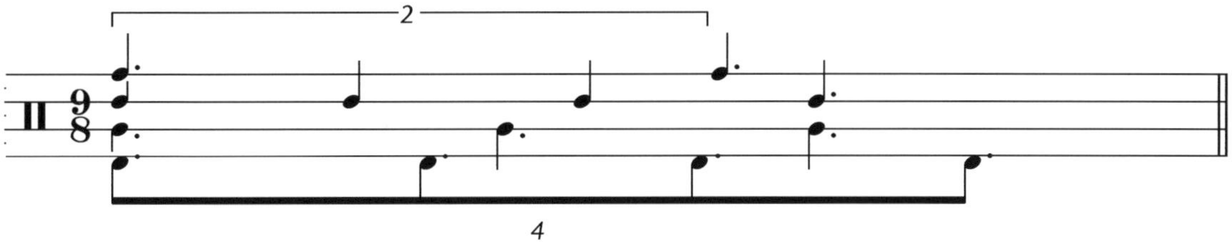

The above examples should be worked on thoroughly. The information will then be transferable to all other metres. After you master the above information your ability to perform in the common metres of 4/4 and 3/4 will also be greatly enhanced, and your music skills will have grown to a new level. See the composition A Journey *in chapter 20, p. 50.*

CHAPTER 17

Subdivision and Metric Modulation in 10/8

10/8 is double 5/8. All the subdivisions and metric modulations in 5/8 also apply to this metre, see chapter 8. The metre has more possibilities because there are ten beats to subdivide. Ex. 83 below gives four subdivided examples of bass-line type phrases in 10/8: 3-3-3-3-2-3-3; 3-3-2-2-3-3-2-2; 3-3-3-2-2-3-2; 2-3-2-3-2-3-2-3. Use the appropriate *Konokol* syllables for each subdivision. Bar 4 below is subdivided into four groups of five sixteenth notes suggesting the metric modulation 4:10. Set a metronome at 150 bpm.

Musical Example

Ex. 83

42

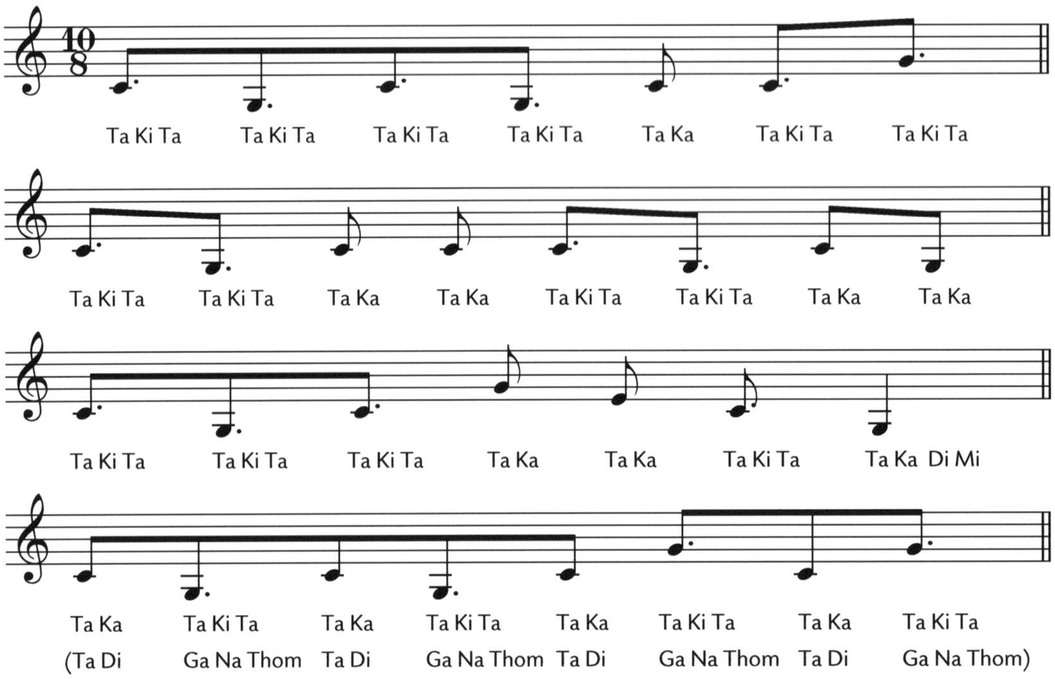

The 10/8 metre is double the odd metre 5/8 and 10/4 is double 5/4. In Ex. 83 above the bass line is grouped into two sets of five quarter note phrases. It has smaller subdivisions (thirty-second note groupings) of the beat than previously seen. These smaller subdivisions should be applied to the other odd metres.

CHAPTER 18

Subdivision and Metric Modulation in 11/8

When time signatures are extended there is a tendency to subdivide them into two or more parts. This is similar to the 5/4 time signature in chapter 3 where the beat is counted as a bar of 3/4 and 2/4.

The previous methods of subdivision and metric modulation should be applied to this metre. The first bar of Ex. 84 below is grouped as a 5½/4 metre (2-2-2-2-3). Certain songs lend themselves better to odd metre arrangement and it depends on the structure of the melody.

In bar 2 below the dotted quarter note is in the middle and similar to the Bulgarian *Kopanitsa* rhythm. Set a metronome at 220 bpm on an eleven beat cycle representing quarter notes. A repeated bar will equal one cycle.

Ex. 84

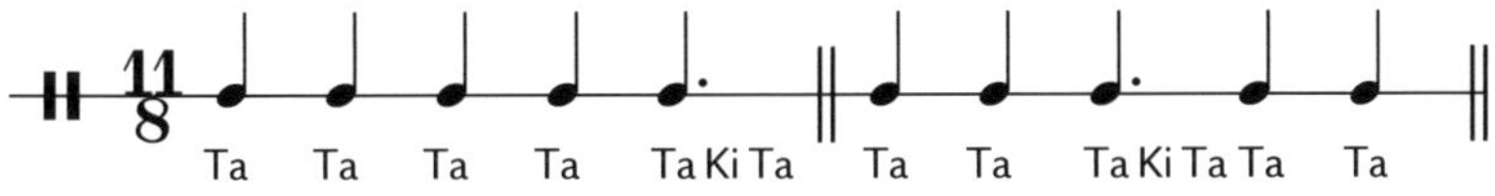

43

The first bar above can be viewed as a 2/4 bar (first two quarter notes) and a bar of 3½/4 (third and fourth quarter notes and dotted quarter note). Or it can be viewed as a 3/4 bar and a 2½/4 bar. Subdividing the bar into two time signatures is generally the case when counting longer metres because the shorter metres are more familiar and comfortable to play. A lot also depends on the tempo of the song.

Note: If the time signature of 5½/4 is halved the metre will be 2¾/2. When halving a time signature of 11/8 to 5½/4, and further to 2¾/2, it is important to realise that the eighth note does not change but represents a different division of the beat in each time signature. For example, an eighth note represents a single beat in 11/8, half a beat in 5½/4, and quarter of a beat in 2¾/2.

When the tempo is slower in 11/8 or other extended metres, there is a tendency to double the tempo. For musical examples of 11/8 and 5½/4, see the composition Kopanypso *in chapter 20, p. 51, which is composed in a fast Kopanitsa rhythm and the composition* The Meeting *in chapter 20, p. 52.*

Chapter 19
Subdivision and Metric Modulation in 13/8 and 15/8

13/8 is an extended metre and the beat can be subdivided into various rhythmic combinations, for example, 4-4-5 or 2-2-3-2-2-2, suggesting a bar of 6½/4 subdivided into a bar of 3½/4 and a bar of 3/4. The first three bars in Ex. 84 below are subdivided into 2-2-3-2-2-2 while the fourth bar is subdivided into 2-2-2-2-2-3 which gives a metre of 6½/4.

13/8 can also be counted as 6½/4 subdivided into 2-2-2-2-2-3 (1-1-1-1-1-1-½) or 3¼/2 – 4-4-4-1 (1-1-1-¼). Count with the appropriate rhythmic syllables for each grouping. Set a metronome at 120 bpm representing quarter notes (13/4). Note that every second bar is on the up beat.

Musical Example

Ex. 85

44

15/8 is triple 5/8 and, as with 10/8, the modulations and subdivisions given for 5/8, chapter 8, apply here also.

The metre can be counted as 15/8, 7½/4 or 3¾/2, depending on the desired rhythmic grouping of a composition or arrangement. The 15 beats can be subdivided into 5-5-5 (suggesting a metric modulation of 3:15) or as in the composition *It Could Be True,* 7-8 (chapter 20, p. 53), which is subdivided further into 2-2-3-2-2-2-2. Other subdivisions include: 6-5-4 (3-3-2-3-2-2); 2-2-2-2-2-2-3 (or 1-1-1-1-1-1-½) – 7½/4; 4-3-4-3-1; 4-4-4-3 (or 1-1-1-¾) – 3¾/2 and so on. In the above subdivided examples the numbers may of course be switched around to achieve a desired rhythm.

The composition *It Could Be True* is mostly subdivided into 2-2-3-2-2-2-2 (a bar of 3½/4 and 4/4).

Longer metres can be subdivided into many groupings depending on the desired rhythmic effect. Subdividing longer metres into two or more shorter metres is the norm. Remember that regardless of the subdivisions in a time signature, the melodic phrasing must extend over a full bar to justify using that time signature. Use the methods given in previous chapters to develop metric modulations. It is best to start by dividing a bar into half.

Chapter 20

Compositions and Arrangements

In this chapter there are six original compositions: *African Way*, *Song For Lieb,* both in 7/4, *Kopanypso* in 11/8, *Switch* in 9/8, *The Meeting* in 11/8 and *It Could Be True* in 15/8; a multiple metric modulation: 1:2:3:4:5:6:7:8:9:10:11:12, and four bars of a multiple metric modulation in 18/16.

45

African Way

Michael Nielsen

African Way (7/4)

African Way below contains a repetitive figure while the melody is quite free of its boundaries. It is good practice to play the figure and sing the melody or rhythm of the melody over it. The harmony is in the top voice. Set your metronome at 80 bpm.

Song For Lieb

46

Michael Nielsen

Song For Lieb (7/4)

Song for Lieb is a composition that really wrote itself; after a number of years concentrating on odd metre performance and composition the metre became second nature. The metric modulations, which feature in the melody, happened naturally during the writing process. They give the song freedom and an expression that seems to transcend the metre. I have played this song many times with Dave Liebman. The tempo of the song is 190 bpm.

47

A Journey

Michael Nielsen

A Journey (9/8)

See below the composition, *A Journey*. The subdivision is 2-2-2-3, 3-3-3, or 3-2-2-2 (bars 17 and 21). Your ability to count the dotted quarter note in any position of the bar should be developed. Set a metronome at 100 bpm, representing quarter notes (4½/4) where the half beat is at the end of the count. Keep the rhythmic pulse of the subdivision 2-2-2-3 throughout.

48

Kopanypso

Michael Nielsen

A **Fast**

Bass plays 4/3/4; follow displaced 3 in B section

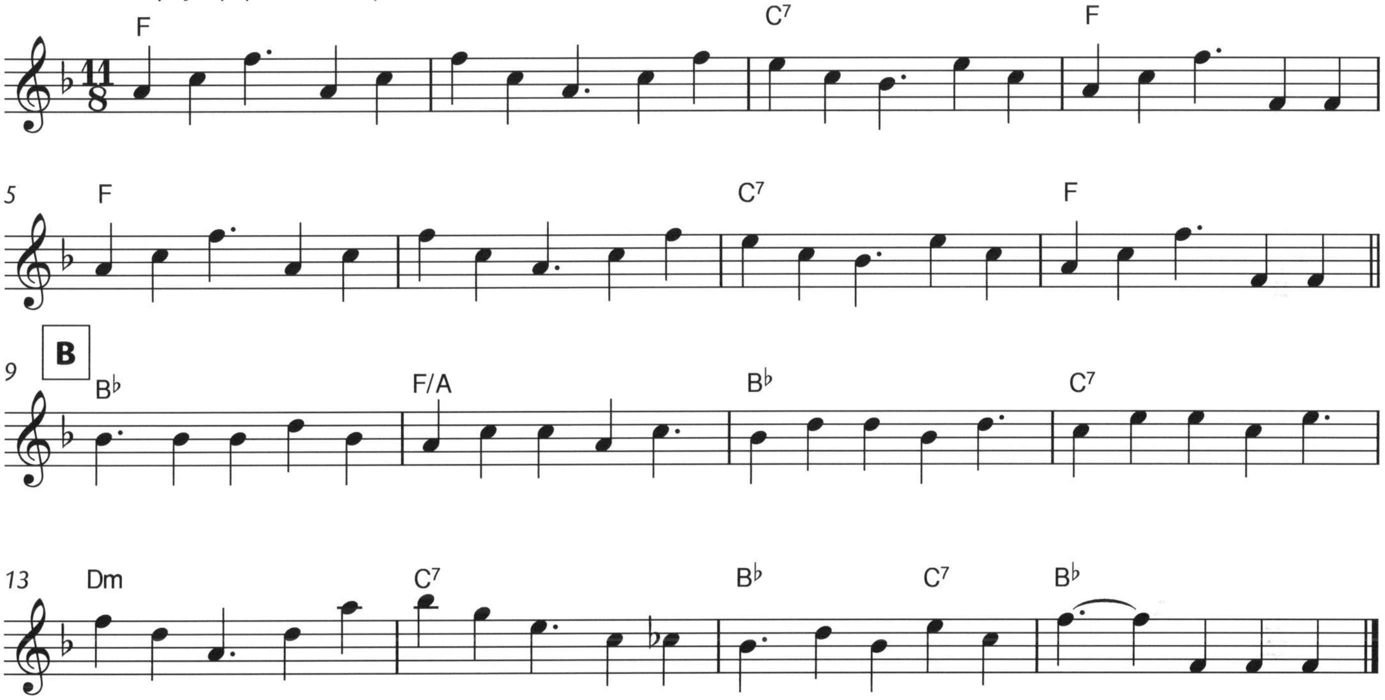

Kopanypso (11/8)

The following composition is in a fast 11/8 *Kopanitsa* rhythm (bars 1–8). From bar 9 onwards the melody features the dotted beat in different places. Before playing the piece of music set a metronome on a rhythm 2-2-3-2-2 at 555 bpm and practise speaking the rhythm using the syllables: *Ta-Ka-Di-Mi – Ta-Ki-Ta – Ta-Ka-Di-Mi* for bars 1-8, 13 and 14; *Ta-Ki-Ta – Ta-Ka-Di-Mi – Ta-Ka-Di-Mi* for bars 9 and 15; *Ta-Ka-Di-Mi – Ta-Ka-Di-Mi – Ta-Ki-Ta* for bars 10, 11 and 12, and *Ta-Di-Ga-Na-Thom – Ta-Ka – Ta-Ka-Di-Mi* for the last bar.

49

The Meeting

Michael Nielsen

The Meeting (5½/4)

The following composition represents a thirty-two bar jazz standard song in 11/8. *The Meeting* is simply arranged into a 2-2-2-2-3 subdivision in 11/8. Two bars of a standard song in 4/4 time equal one bar of 5½/4. When the tempo of a 5½/4 time signature is slow the tendency is to double the tempo, which gives, in this particular song, a swing tempo in 11/8 – similar to doubling the time in 4/4. Many jazz standards can be arranged in this way. Set your metronome at 130 bpm representing quarter notes.

It Could Be True (15/8)

It Could Be True is subdivided mostly into 2-2-3-2-2-2-2, which gives a bar of 3½/4 and a bar of 4/4. It also could be counted as 3¾/2, 4-3-4-4, or 1-¾-1-1 using the syllables, *Ta – Ta-Ki-Ta – Ta – Ta*, where *Ta* represents the beat (four eighth notes) and *Ta-Ki-Ta* represents three eighth notes. An extended coda is added which features many different groupings and where chords are suspended across the bar line. Set a metronome at 104 bpm representing quarter notes (7½/4) where the extra half beat is at the end.

50

It Could Be True

Michael Nielsen

Chapter 21
Multiple Metric Modulations in 1/1 and 18/16

Ex. 86 below in 1/1 gives metric modulation ratios from one to twelve: 1:2:3:4:5:6:7:8:9:10:11:12. Each modulation increases by 40 bpm and the tempo of the beat of each modulation is given above the stave. When counting stave one, clap on the beat and internally count four beats, this will help to feel the beat at the slow tempo of 40 bpm; always be aware of the half bar division. This exercise is a difficult challenge and to perform it correctly you will need precision timing. It is best to count seven beats using the syllables: *Ta-Ka – Ta-Ka – Ta-Ki-Ta;* nine beats, *Ta-Ki-Ta – Ta-Ki-Ta – Ta-Ki-Ta* and eleven beats, *Ta-Ki-Ta – Ta-Ki-Ta – Ta-Ki-Ta – Ta-Ka.*

Ex. 86

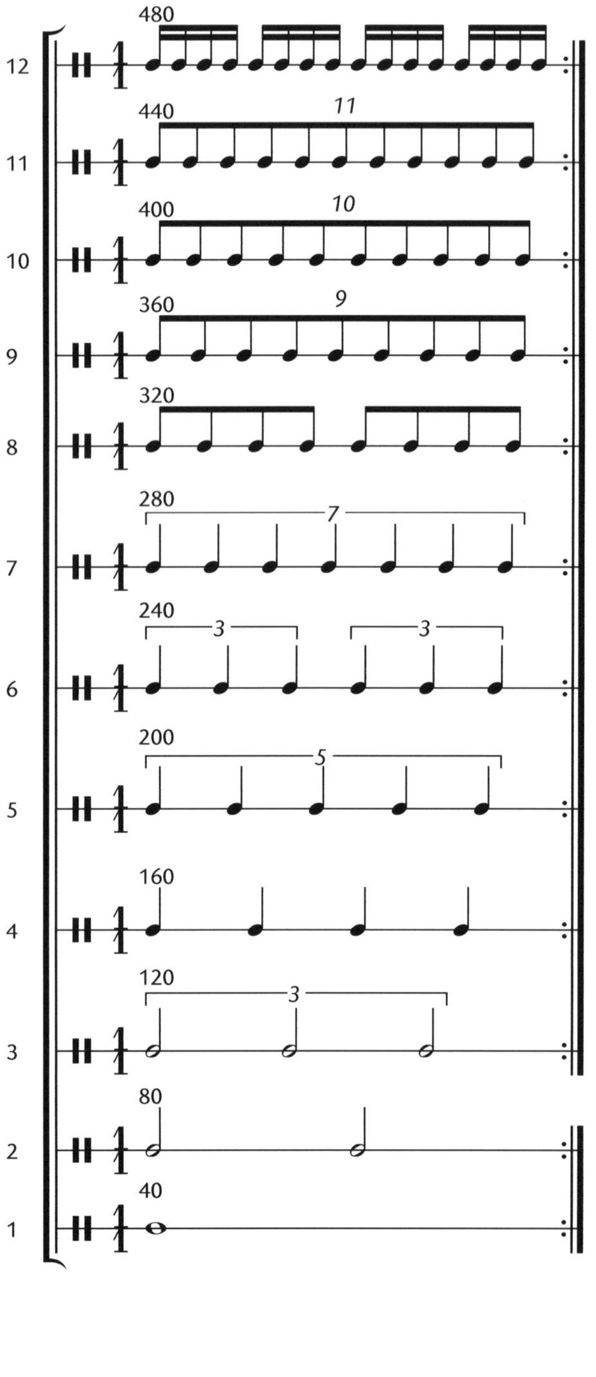

Ex. 87 below shows seven modulation relationships: 1:2:6:3:4½:4:8 in 9/8 or 18/16 arranged for two guitars (or piano), bass and percussion.

Ex. 87

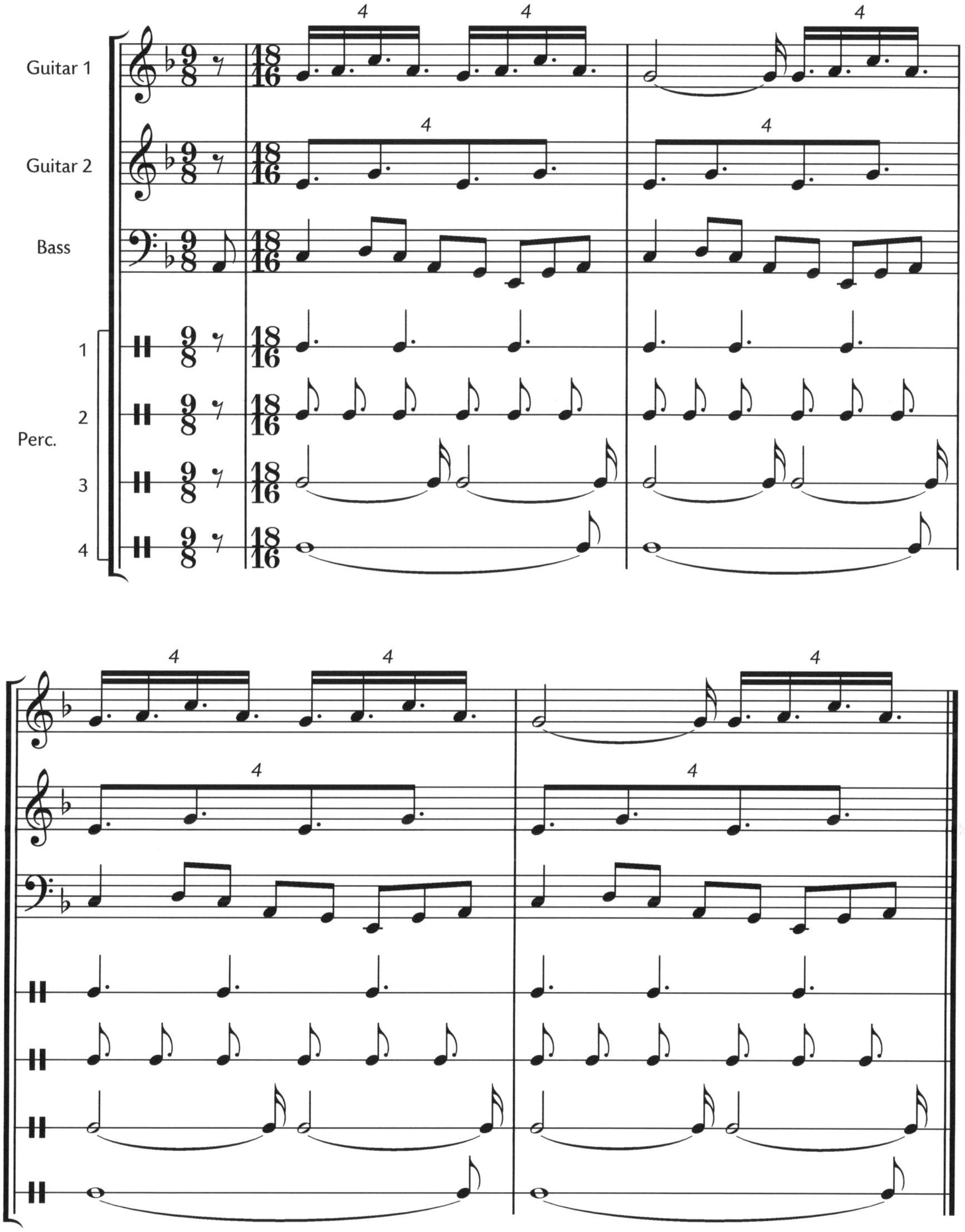

Conclusion

Ultimately, make sure you take time internalizing the contents of each chapter. Remember the information I have formulated and presented in this book took a number of years to accumulate. Be patient and enjoy the precision-timing trip, it brought me great musical satisfaction, both as a composer and performer, and I hope it does the same for you.

All the best,

Mike Nielsen

(Picture by Lieve Boussauw © b-lieve.be)

Mike Nielsen is coordinator of the Masters in Jazz Performance Degree programme at the Dublin Institute of Technology. He has performed with many leading international jazz artists, most notably Dave Liebman, with whom he has toured Europe, Australia, and New Zealand. He was awarded a Licentiate of Trinity College, London (LTCL) in classical guitar performance and received a scholarship to attend Berklee College of Music, Boston. Mike also holds an MPhil in microtonal theory and physics and a PhD in microtonal improvisation which included the design of original microtonal guitars. He has appeared on 18 recordings, including two with Dave Liebman. He is a prolific composer and his new CD *Acoustic Sound Recipes* features original music.
Email: mikenielsenmusic@gmail.com

Audio Track Listing

1	Introduction
2	The Konokol Syllables
3	Chapter 2 – Ex. 17
4	Chapter 2 – Ex. 18
5	Chapter 3 – Ex. 19
6	Chapter 3 – Ex. 20
7	Chapter 6 – Ex. 29
8	Chapter 6 – Ex. 30
9	Chapter 6 – Ex. 31
10	Chapter 6 – Ex. 32
11	Chapter 7 – Ex. 35
12	Chapter 7 – Ex. 36
13	Chapter 7 – Ex. 37
14	Chapter 7 – Ex. 38
15	Chapter 7 – Ex. 41
16	Chapter 8 – Ex. 45
17	Chapter 8 – Ex. 46
18	Chapter 8 – Ex. 47
19	Chapter 9 – Ex. 51
20	Chapter 9 – Ex. 52
21	Chapter 9 – Ex. 53, bars 1–10
22	Chapter 9 – Ex. 53, bars 11–14
23	Chapter 10 – Ex. 55
24	Chapter 11 – Ex. 58
25	Chapter 11 – Ex. 59
26	Chapter 11 – Ex. 60
27	Chapter 11 – Ex. 61
28	Chapter 11 – Ex. 62
29	Chapter 12 – Ex. 65
30	Chapter 13 – Ex. 68
31	Chapter 13 – Ex. 69
32	Chapter 14 – Ex. 72
33	Chapter 14 – Ex. 73
34	Chapter 14 – Ex. 74
35	Chapter 15 – Ex. 75
36	Chapter 15 – Ex. 76
37	Chapter 15 – Ex. 77
38	Chapter 16 – Ex. 78
39	Chapter 16 – Ex. 79
40	Chapter 16 – Ex. 80
41	Chapter 16 – Ex. 81
42	Chapter 17 – Ex. 83
43	Chapter 18 – Ex. 84
44	Chapter 19 – Ex. 85
45	African Way
46	Song for Lieb
47	A Journey
48	Kopanypso
49	The Meeting
50	It Could Be True